LIFE
THROUGH
THE LONG
WINDOW

Clare Lynch

ORIGINAL WRITING

ISBN: 978-1-906018-26-9

Front cover photography by kind permission of Anna Marie Dowdican

A CIP catalogue for this book is available from the National Library.

Published by Original Writing Ltd., Dublin, 2007.

Printed by Colourbooks, Dublin.

To
those I love

CONTENTS

ACKNOWLEDGEMENTS

Desert Call for 'Shards', *RTE   Lyric Fm* for 'Miss You, Bluebottle', 'Doing Nothing with Bluebirds' and 'Starbucks'. *Desert Call, RTE Lyric FM* and *Ocean FM* for 'Feel Good Houses.'

The author would like to acknowledge the generous support of Sligo Arts Office and The Arts Council for bursaries awarded in 2003.

Thank you to the following:

Anna Marie Dowdican, for her tremendous support, friendship and merciless editorial skills. The Carmelite Communities in both Holy Hill, Skreen, Co Sligo and Nada, Crestone, Colorado, for the combination of generous space, spiritual strength and friendship. Those valued friends who hang out in Skreen, Riverstown, Ballincar, Strandhill and Galway. Tim and Shirley Kerns, for their spirited approach to life. My publishers, Original Writing. Tallahassee Irish Society, for their encouragement and cultural generosity. Máire Nic Gearailt, Maura Gilligan and Dermot Healy for their encouragement and help. Susan Starkey, for the right words at the right time. My cousin Martina for things too numerous to name. My nephews, Thomas and Shane, for spending one whole day of their summer holidays trying to find a title for this book...and all the Tullypole gang for their presence in my life. Pat Mooney, for benevolent support and last but not at all least, God, who has gotten me this far.

INTRODUCTION

BEFORE YOU BEGIN this book ensure you're sitting some place private. Clare Lynch writes with a quirky honesty that has one erupting unexpectedly into either laughter or tears. Her writing has the power to heal a person; even in places they didn't realize needed healing.

She takes ordinary subject matter and entwines it with a humour that is refreshing. Clare patiently attends to the thresholds of the unspeakable in a voice both irreverent and sacred at the same time. May you find some of your hidden and wondrous self in the images shared in these stories.

Susan Starkey

Life Through The Long Window

Borderline Borderland

GREAGHCLOCH WAS THE TOWNLAND with the stone. A place of small fields and farms, stone walls, harrows in hedgerows and rusty bed frames guarding gaps. Morris Minors became hen-houses. Watchful country homes kept a weather eye on rising cattle prices and falling morals. Greaghcloch, Mullagh, Kells, Co Meath. It was contradiction, Mullagh being in Co Cavan, Kells being in Co Meath. We were borderline borderland.

The stone my father said, was on our neighbour's land, past the second field behind his house. A big boulder, half over and half under the earth, it could never be moved by man or beast or bad luck would surely follow. My father left the lone fairy tree standing on our fourth field to show solidarity with the stone on our neighbours land. Tree and stone, they weathered superstition together and lived powerful lives of greater or lesser fabled animation. It was borderline land all the time.

I remember one day on that long narrow lane between our neighbour's farm and our own I met the squad car coming down. I stood well in on the mearin ditch to give it room to pass. The garda behind the wheel rolled down his window:

Had I noticed any strange cars going up or down the lane in the past few days, he asked me. *Had there been anyone around?* I knew nothing, said less. He told me I was a lovely girl and drove unhurriedly down towards the road, avoiding the rough potholes of the country lane in order to preserve his Ford Sierra for further abuse on some other Cavan surface.

My father told me later that there'd been a big heap of IRA arms found up the lane, hidden in bales in an old shed. The area was full of IRA sympathisers on account of the hunger strikers. It wasn't strangers the guards were looking for at all, he said, and well they knew it. But they had to be seen to be doing their job though in the end nothing would be done about anything. And nothing was.

I watched the news for days and days afterwards. Bobby Sands had just died and things were heavy. It took an effort to watch something that wasn't *The Two Ronnies* or *The Live Mike*, but I bore with it. There might be news, like I mean, interesting news. There might be a reporter standing at the end of our farm lane saying about '*the unprecedented amount of firearms recently discovered in this quiet rural area.*' There might be, say, a close-up snapshot of our postman, or Ned the mobile shop man or maybe even McCarthy the A.I. man, because my father said that it was a local was at the back of it. I suspected them all, even the parish priest and the creamery man.

But no. Oh no. RTE was having none of it. It was all Paisley and Thatcher and Thatcher and Paisley and factories closing here there and everywhere but nothing about anyone being arrested over an arms raid in Greaghcloch, the borderline borderland, townland with the stone.

The whole thing annoyed me. Why hadn't I been the one to uncover the guns, on a walk with Buff the Labrador? That would've surely got me a slot in the Mullagh news column in the Anglo Celt at the very least. And maybe our picture on the front, sitting on a load of sawn-off shot guns smiling for the camera. Buff could hold things in his mouth fairly reliably without chewing them. He would've even looked good with a grenade.

But no. We never got our chance to shine. It seemed that

in every way, Greaghcloch had failed to put itself on the map and would continue its undefined existence of things half hidden, half exposed.

SECOND-HAND LIVES

MY MOTHER wasn't an alcoholic or a gambler and possessed no other corruptive vice that I can recall, but boys oh boys was she a junkie when it came to second-hand shops.

We would go in together on Saturdays to the Aladdin's cave that was Johnson's. The door opened with a ding-dong of a broken-voiced bell. Inside, discombobulated customers slowly manoeuvred their way through a domestic sea of three-piece suites, wall units and bedside lockers; touching surfaces reverentially with the air of people visiting a cemetery. They bent to slide open and shut a drawer, to snap apart the lead-lined glass doors on a drinks cabinet or question the hinges on a bedside locker. Every now and again my eyes met with the surreal sight of a customer sinking down flat onto a bed, fully clothed in anorak, slacks and Clarks shoes; then rising like Dracula moments later, smiling as if coming out of some delicious daytime slumber.

Johnson's had aspirations to being an antique shop—bulking out its claim with fat-lipped ugly Toby jugs, pewter plates and cracked willow pattern oddities. Fiddly-handled china with room for barely a tweaked little finger so out of place in Cavan but I was fascinated by the dexterity of the posh bony-handed folk who may have once used it. It was accompanied by three-tiered cake stands with intricate bucolic scenery on each plate, hounds, huntsmen, that class of thing. My mother bought such a cake-stand and it lived out its genteel retirement in our house quite unused in the good cabinet in the good room where nothing was ever used because it was too good to be broken.

Throughout the shop was the pungent bouquet that is unique to such establishments, consisting as it did of undertones of mice, Silvo, wood polish, damp, tobacco, and other people's scent. Smoky old mirrors wrapped in newspaper, oil lamps with broken globes and chairs that had lost their spring in some overloaded yesteryear sat forlornly throughout the shop like children waiting to be collected after school. My delight lay in discovering the writing cases, snuff boxes, broken music boxes and the chess sets. I loved it best when I could sneak down to the pianos and play a three-note complicated made-up composition that could only otherwise be handled by Liberace. He was the only pianist I had ever heard of and it took all the sophistication I had to impersonate him. Even the piano's plink plonk out-of-tuneness added to its artistic merit, as if it were throwing a sulk and refusing to play its troubled ivory heart out in such a place as this.

Every week without fail I managed to buy something, usually a hard backed detective novel from the Herbert Jenkins stable. The original reader's name inscribed in copperplate on the flyleaf, the date maybe from the nineteen twenties. At home, I added my own name with whatever style of handwriting I thought aesthetic enough to accompany theirs. From there, I settled back to enjoy the yesterdayness of the murder mystery; the tweeds, the single shot from a gun, the fashionably dressed heroine, the two-dimensional nature of the fiendishly twisting plot and—all the way through—the tantalising smell of the aged pages. In such books, the detective always got his man—or his woman—and it was accomplished with no silly messing around, psychoanalysing or laboriously sidetracking with his own personal problems or tedious descriptions of what he had with his dinner or why his first marriage hadn't worked out.

One Saturday I came across something that was quite a

world away from a detective novel. It was a canister in a tough green canvas-covered pouch. Unremarkable from the outside. I popped the lid on the can, thinking how perfect a size it was for holding my pens and drawing pencils. A square of paper was glued to the inside of the lid. It was a woman's address, typed in that emphatic old way typewriters used to type everything. *Miss Jane Smyth, 34 High St, Linlithgow.* There was a post code too. Apart from that, the canister was empty, a sweet smell of dry unusedness about it. I studied it again. There was a picture of an aeroplane on the top of the lid. I looked closer and felt my blood chill.

It wasn't exactly an aeroplane, it was a war plane. There was wording under it, small and black: *Todd Gas Mask Container.*

From Johnson's second hand shop in 1980s Bailieborough, I felt like I was suddenly transported back to 1930s Scotland, to the horror of being Miss Jane Smyth and receiving this object. Looking at it and realising my country was at war.

I bought the gas mask container for fifty pence and took it back home to live its second-hand life as a holder for all my drawing implements.

That's what second hand shops give you. The shell of someone else's life. The teasing incompleteness of wondering about the first person who played that piano, sniffed from that snuff box, wrote with that scratchy dip pen. We are left holding particles of other people's lives in our good cabinets like bone fragments, trying to piece together the skeleton, and then attempting to attach the flesh. All I have is a tin can. And a wide open wonder as to the life that first encountered it at a time when history was being changed forever.

Notions

Hannigan is my name, Paddy Hannigan.

I come from a tidy little place on the back road to Mohill. We're nicely in off the main road and the bus passes the house. Handy enough for mammy because her legs doesn't be good with the veins. We have a grand size of a back yard. It has great room for turning the hearse and reversing in and out. Indeed we are blessed in this respect.

There's many's a woman is mad after me for what I'll have when my mother's day is gone, but I'm only fifty five and I'm tellin' you, I'll not rush into anything sudden. Oh no, boy, not me.

If you want to know the cut of a man I am, I suppose I might as well lay it out for you here and now. I'm as thin as a lath. If I turned sideways you wouldn't see me. Six foot three in my stockinged feet. I have a class of pale skin that's inclined to get a bit moist in summer or under them new fangled spotlights in modern kitchens. People do keep their houses too hot, I find. I always bring a pocket handkerchief with me when I go out to these wake houses and it does be pure wringing with the sweat when I get back to my own place that night. My hair is like a mare's tail. That's what Mammy sez, anyway. It blows its warp and weft over my forehead whenever the wind is from Mohill. I do what I can to flatten it out with brilliantine, but sometimes that wee bald spot breaks through like a fresh egg. These comb-over styles do be hard enough to maintain. Ach, I suppose I must bear it. Though I think the wee bit of hair loss makes me look quite a bit older than I am.

My nose is commanding enough. It's a sharp one, that's for sure. I'm cut from a coin in that regard. I have my grandfather's square bony shoulders and the walk of the Gilligans on my mother's side. A bit of a goosestep. They call me 'The Long Fella' behind my back but I don't mind it one bit because Dev did a lot of good for this country, God rest him.

The mammy says I have a forehead with more ridges than a washboard but I tell her, 'mammy, you don't know the half of it...you have no idea how much pressure I'm under in my line of work. Why wouldn't I have a few wrinkles with all that does be on my mind?'

When a person ups and dies, I must be about things, whether day or night. Sure none of you ordinary people understand what's involved. The gravediggers, the flowers, the shaking of the hands and the sandwiches for the wake...the organising of all that is left to me, you know. It's a very delicate thing to get all right and offend no one at the same time. Remembering who's the widow and who's only the old flame and where to sit them that they won't tear the eyes out of one another's head.

I'm tellin' you, you have no idea.

I never miss Mass of a Sunday. I get to meet and greet the people there and find out who's poorly or who's taken bad. It's a place to keep abreast of business. I sit halfways down the chapel on the men's side and I can tell by the 'V' in the back of a fella's neck if he has long left in him. I can gauge it to within two weeks, which is fairly good if I do say so myself. I don't go up to communion until near the last. That way I can see the walk of everyone in the parish and how they've failed or who's lost a sight of weight in their overcoat. I know the signs, I'm telling you an' I never miss a trick. Sure I can't afford to, my business really is about life or death.

Now, you don't need to know a lot else about me but maybe I'll tell you another wee bit seeing as how you have the time to listen and you can already tell I'm an interesting man. When I was young, I had my heart broken by a heart scald of a woman. I was hardly twenty five when I met Rosie Foley at the Pioneer Social in the Farmer's Hall. Wasn't I only a cub. She got me dancing with her and all that foolyaddlum and sure we went out with one another for a while afterwards. Well, what I mean to say is, we started courting and went out together for fifteen years. Then one day she gets on her high horse and says she wants a ring on her finger.

A ring on her finger, if you don't mind!

And I says to her, 'What hurry's on you, sure aren't we going fine as we are, nice and handy?'

But she ates the face of me and tells me that all her school friends are married and nearly grandmothers at this stage and says on top of all that nonsense that I'm not much of a man if I can't give her a commitment.

A 'commitment,' if you please!

Fine big fancy word like that, she must've met the scholars comin' home because it's not for all the schoolin' she got herself that she'd learn such a grand word.

And I said the truth back to her. I says I couldn't give her a 'commitment.' I'm not the kind of man to rush into things.

And she back in my face tells me that I couldn't pull the skin off a rice pudding.

She left me like that.

That was over fourteen years ago and I'm tellin' you, I'm not the better of that wretched woman ever since. I do often see her peddling into the town there of a Friday, with the big head of hair on her under the headscarf. She and Bartley the brother lived for years together in the home place out Lisnabuntry way. The Jobber Foleys is what they were known as. Ah now, they never amounted to much, for all their high notions.

Do you know what my own father used to say a notion was?

'A lot of water on the brain.'

Aye. 'A lot of water on the brain, young Paddy, a lot of water on the brain,' is what he always said. God rest him, whenever he thought I was getting high-minded in my ways as a young fella.

But let me go on with my story anyway.

Only a month ago in the town, didn't I get the word. Rosie Foley's brother died sudden. Dropped dead in the wee garden at the back of the house and him out setting cabbages. It was Jack the Post had the news to me maybe only half an hour after it happened. He'd seen Dr Murray's car and all the commotion going on at Foley's so he turned in at their lane to see what was the stir. Massive heart attack, that's what he was told. Without any delay at all I shot home and changed into my white shirt— the mammy does a great job of starching the collar—so I knew I'd come across well. I had the good suit from Finnegan's only on me when the call came to the house.

'My deepest condolences, may he rest in peace, Miss Foley,' is what I said to Rosie on the phone. 'I'll be up to you in under fifteen minutes.'

I find that people get great comfort out of seeing the under-taker coming out quick to the house. They need leadership at a time like that. I'm always there with the right words. It's a gift I have. I shake hands with everybody and I listen hard to get the names right. There's people I don't remember, but I never let on that I don't know their names. Oh no! That'd be disaster; you could lose business over the head of it when their time would come. No. There's always a way of finding out and I'm the man that's great at it.

When I landed into Foley's yard, there was a few ones of the neighbours gathering already. I rubbed my hands together into a good tight ball, trying to get them warmed up a bit. I have fierce bad circulation, God help me.

I shook hands with Rosie all right and she was upset sure enough. I said all the right things to her. I told her what a com-fort it was for her to have him so long and what a great brother he was for all them years, how he'd always pick her up from the town if it was raining and how nice and tasty he kept their wee house and garden. Oh I was saying all the right things when she turned on me with that scaldy look in her eye and said to me, 'Fat lot of comfort that is to me when he's gone!'

Ach! I paid no heed of her, she's a contrary type of article and sure people can get a bit upset when ones belonging to them dies.

'Come in,' I says to her, 'to my stockroom at your convenience and we'll make the necessary decisions. I'll give you a lift in the hearse; sure I have it parked right outside....'

I have a large display room to one side of my brother's pub and grocery. Very impressive if I do say so myself. We Hannigans have been in the business for three generations and we have a tight reputation for hard work and thrift. 'No flies on us only dead ones.' as they say in these parts.

I showed her my line of coffins.

'We have a beautiful deep lined casket in oak, satin-lining, polished brass handles and an inlay of the twelve apostles...' I told her, showing her my top of the range box. I couldn't help running my hand over the heads of Jesus and John to emphasise the fine workmanship. It's quite a magnificent casket and many's the occasion I've imagined myself reposing in it when my time comes. I'd be entitled to a very attractive staff discount, you see.

She looked squarely at it. 'He was a simpler man nor that,' she said to me.

I showed her a middle of the range model. No inlay. Just the brass handles and plate.

'It's exceptionally well priced,' I told her. 'It allows for a fine presentation of your departed Loved One. With three fresh wreaths on top, it's very eye-catching.

'They're not coming to have their eyes caught,' she said to me, kind of sharpish. I didn't take to her tone.

'And there'll be no fresh flowers with my asthma being the way it is.'

There was nothing for it but to show her my cheapest caskets. 'Oak veneer,' I said to her. 'It closely resembles the real thing. Imitation brass handles...and if he's laid out in his Sunday suit there'll be no need for the shroud...'

'It was made with him in mind,' she said simply. 'You may bring it on to the house with you and make sure'n throw in two of them plastic wreaths. A round one and a cross. Won't we be leaving a lot of money in your brother's lounge bar this week-end; you needn't be looking at me like that! Oh aye! And six white sliced pans, two pound of butter and a lock of ham...'

Oh but it's the honest truth. I couldn't help but stare at her... What a fine looking woman she was with that head of grey curls peeking out from under the horseshoe headscarf. Those brazen blue eyes! Shapely legs in that tweed skirt from all the cycling and Irish dancing she does. She wouldn't be much over the fifty mark...plenty of working years left in her. I was appalled to discover that she had power over me yet. What a fine couple we could make still....And sure she had that lovely wee house of the Foley's and the bit of land; wouldn't the home place fall to her now with the brother gone? With her as thrifty as myself, we could build on to the back of the stockroom in jig time and have a lovely funeral parlour with beige wallpaper and some nice Phil Coulter music playing for the deceased. Not to mention the fine hard-working woman she'd be around the house and how well she'd be able to look after the mammy when poor mammy would get that little bit older. The fortune we'd save on the nursing home.

It was as if at this very minute the Good Lord was telling me that I was ready for marriage, directing me to it by His holy hand. I hadn't felt this excited in myself since Leitrim made it through to the Connaught semi-final. It was my first time—oh and I'm almost ashamed to say it out to you now—to fall madly in love.

'Rosie,' I said to her, my heart almost smothered in my chest. I caught up her right hand in my two cold ones and held it tightly, a bit to her surprise.

'Rosie,' I said to her, 'I'm fierce sorry for all you're going through at the minute...my thoughts are with you in your grief, indeed, indeed, indeed, but I just want to tell you...just want you to know...that I'm ready for that commitment. I'm willing to marry you whenever you'll agree...'

She snatched her hand out of mine in a mad rush and looked at me with the angry eye of a goat looking into a potato pit. Oh, I'll remember the following words for a long time yet...

'You ould humpy amadan!' she shouted at me. 'Commitment, is it? It's committed you should be, with your daft bloody notions!'

And she swung away from me like that, shouting back over her shoulder:

'Come on, look lively now and give me a lift back to the house, haven't I plenty to be doin'? Don't forget the sliced pans and the ham!'

As if I were no more than a serving boy. That was in or around four weeks ago and I'm not the better of it still.

Mammy knew right well there was something vexing me. She shook her head when I told her.

'Ah Paddy, Paddy, what used your father tell you about notions?' she asked me, 'what used he tell you?'

'Ach, Mammy, you have no idea what I'm suffering,' I told her, 'Not the foggiest.'

That contrary old Rosie Foley.

Heart scald of a woman.

When her time comes I'll put thorns in her casket.

REAL CURVES AND FAKE TAN

I'M SURE MOST WOMEN KNOW what it's like. The summons. To the wedding. Of a size ten cousin smothered in size ten sisters and mothered by a Pekinese aunt. The kind of cousin who's getting carefully married to an overachieving spouse— the CEO of some frightfully successful company. The kind of cousin who purges herself of any real food until her shadow is the biggest part of her and is only happy with her weight when her cheekbones are sharp enough to cut bacon. On top of that, she's the kind of cousin who will tilt her head sideways and say,

'My word, Brenda, you'll have to cut back on those pastries, you'll never get a man looking like that.'

Every well-toned, gym-addicted male sibling in her family drives a state of the art jeep whilst all the stringy women folk drive sporty little Italian efforts so boastfully ergonomic that they probably run on their own spit.

Where does that put me and my faithful Mazda with its clapped out exhaust and the passenger door that won't lock from the outside?

I wish I didn't have to go.

I really, really wish I didn't.

Oh can't entire summers be spoiled by such kin?

And well-meaning folk around me saying:

'You have a wedding on? Well, that's something to look forward to. Lucky old you. Have you bought any style for it yet? Who are ya bringin' with ya?'

Lucky old me?

No, I haven't bought any style cos I'm afraid of my figure in a public changing room and as to whom I'm bringing with me, it's a tough choice between my raggedy Ann doll or my ten year old deaf blind super-farting Labrador. It must be five years since I've been on a date with a decent single man. Oh, plenty of men alright but it turned out a lot of them weren't decent and many of them weren't so single either.

So, I tell you, when it comes to weddings, luck is not exactly a lady. She's a spinstery ould bitch with her resentful claws out, that's what she is.

This evening saw me in front of the half-size dressing table mirror, the only mirror of any decent substance in my apartment; which I bobbed and weaved in front of, squatted, stood up upon a chair in front of, sucked my stomach in, in front of, listed sideways with enigmatic facial expressions in front of...all in my new beige linen dress but to no avail. I still looked like a funfair-sized blob of rough puff pastry.

The dress is out.

It is definitely out.

Even the gridlock underwear couldn't hold me back from the tide of belly bulge. Well, it disguised the belly bulge but carried the tidal wave upwards in order to turn me into a quatro-breasted woman. I could hear my internal critic going crazy with snide remarks.

So take your pick, you want to look eight months pregnant or else an alien from planet mammary?

The alternative is easy. Claim a fatal illness/abduction/emigration or accident on the day of the wedding.

Send the present in the post a few hours after ringing the news in as a gesture of goodwill.

Go to bed with a self-pity size box of Cadbury Celebrations and contemplate irony in a rather obsessive way.

Everyone in the office was raving on about the latest fake tan from *La Finesse*.

There they were at work today, all looking like dodgy foreign no-hopers who should be shifting stolen gear down the back alleys after dusk. Even my sixty-five year old second cousin three and a half times removed was extolling its virtues to me on the phone last night from down the country:

'I do think that new stuff is great,' she told me: 'Everyone at mass was telling me they didn't recognise me under the mighty colour I had. They thought maybe it was from chemotherapy or something but I told them it was from a bottle of *La Finesse*. Brenda, lovie, you that's a bit on the pale side, would you not think about givin' yourself a going-over with it for Amelia's weddin'? Wouldn't it be the makings of you? Wouldn't it, now?'

So, because most women live lives of quiet-and-white-desperation, this evening saw me in the shopping centre looking for the fake tan. Pharmacies make me feel queasy at the best of times, but the one in the centre has a sales assistant who looks like she's been made over by a morgue technician. Her eyelashes are so spiky and stiff that I was afraid she'd put my eye out, let alone her own.

However, the good news for me was that it seemed as though *La Finesse* was practically infallible. A miracle-product. Antennae-Girl bagged it with impeccably lacquered talons whilst assuring me in a mid-Atlantic accent that it *'would achieve great results even on older skin.'*

Later in the privacy of my own bathroom massaging this miracle substance into my flesh, I started worrying about whether I had a biblical disease. It was like my epidermis was falling off. More flakings than makings. There I was, shedding skin like a snake. Confetti-sized blobs of me were quickly littering the bathroom floor.

As for actual skin colour, I was leaning towards the random pattern-making of camouflage. If the entire armed forces had invited themselves in to my bathroom and showed me via mud, cow dung and vegetable dyes how to 'colour myself beautiful' I couldn't have ended up looking worse.

Where was my gentle '*sun-kissed*' glow? In the only half-decent mirror I once again did my bob and weave but could only see the usual pasty ole bits of me wobbling right back. I combated this negative result with the only immediate action a gal like me takes in times such as this: Ignore all product instructions, lash on half the bottle, then sink a bottle of cheap white wine. After thus self-medicating I went to bed blithely optimistic that Mother Nature would find her own miraculous means of turning me into a bombshell before the wedding.

Well, she didn't.

No. In fact she left my weight strictly as it had been, adding to it by giving me a puffy alcohol-fuelled face and a unjustifiably bad hair start. But where she excelled herself was in the colour of my skin. The half-decent mirror tried not to wobble with laughter as it revealed me to be as brown as one of Michael Palin's travel crew. Yes, I looked a few shekels short of the full currency alright. I had to do a sickie from work. At least it wasn't an outright lie when I rang in and told my boss I was feeling off colour.

Here I am three days later; wedding still looming but colour receding. I'm better able to handle the whole deal cos I resurrected a forgotten outfit that I will be wearing to the wedding. My real self. Fits all sizes I might ever happen to be.

FEEL GOOD HOUSES

MY FATHER HAD CURES. What all he couldn't cure could be written on a postage stamp with room left over for Webster's Dictionary.

We lived in the depths of countryside, off a quiet road, up a steep lane, on top of a high hill. It was a lonely road that ribboned for miles between drumlins. Of a summer's evening my brother and I got great joy from watching the occasional car slowing down, down, down, until at the end of our lane it took the turn in and up. We sniggered from behind the shedding geranium in the front kitchen window as the car revved in desperation against the steep gradient. The collie observed the vehicle with his usual disdain from the redcurrant bush at the head of our Khyber Pass.

Eventually landed in our front yard, from the car would emerge some injured party—usually a footballer or aspiring farmer, hobbling badly. The hobblers came for the cure of the sprain. My father was a legend for curing it. It always gave me a sense of awe to observe him—such a big man; with stout labourer's fingers cut by barbed wire and life experience, greased with engine oil, pungent with farm smells—kneeling on the floor in front of some stranger.

He usually placed them in front of the Stanley. Bruce, the rather over-indulged Jack Russell, would observe the scene from beneath the range. It silenced all of us to be in the presence of The Cure as it took place.

My father slashed away at the Sign of The Cross three times before he murmured his prayer, easing his touch down the injured limb. The cure ended with an equal amount of Signs of The Cross to balance things out. The visitor—who might have arrived into our kitchen hopping with the aid of an upturned sweeping brush—often left with just a slight limp. No money changed hands.

'What can I give you for that?'

'Put that away,'

'Ah, Jasus, come on, you'll take something.'

'Indeed'n' I'll not. Don't vex me.'

'You're horrid dacent.'

No, he never asked anything for what he saw as being a gift from the Lord. But his heart would gladden and his eye light up at the sight of a bottle of decent whiskey. More often than not, a glass of that whiskey would be shared with the visitors and a convivial atmosphere ensue.

It was exciting to see these strangers enter our home humbled by their need. By the time they were leaving they were regarded almost as old friends. Some connection was surely made somewhere, let it be from far out acquaintances, a distant blood tie or maybe even some business with a common cattle-dealer or second hand tractor. Such visitors travelled from areas as far as thirty miles away, which to our child's logic were Magi distances, surely. We even had people from 'The North'—a surreal place we thought only existed on the Nine O'Clock News.

My father made other cures—stopping of haemorrhaging, warts, bed-wetting and the burn. I remember him collecting field mice and storing them in Cara matchboxes for one such cure. For another he used black snails, which had to be gathered in early morning. The cupboard above his armchair held cartridges, rosary beads and matchboxes with shrivelled-up creatures.

To see him making up his blend at the kitchen table was like watching a demonic scientist happily at play.

Yet things worked, for all their strangeness.

I think for me what I loved best about those cure days was the sense of community they brought to our house. It was also a gentle lesson in faith and the humility to believe in something that took place outside the power of ourselves. The traffic that trawled our otherwise lonely road gave credence to the fact that as people we all needed each other.

Walking Through Water

I HAD WALKED OVER cobbled sand on a glorious summer's day, had sauntered out maybe a mile. The day was balmy, beautiful and surreal. Like an ancient street under my feet, the cobbled ridges had an infinity to them that was mesmerising. This sea street led all the way to America. Imagine!

I turned back to walk in to the shore only to find that the tide had beaten me to it. The shimmering water was already in close to the shoreline, cutting me off on the flattest of islands. Maybe it was a mirage? My mind wasn't willing to accept it as real. I walked through shallow water at first, delightfully refreshing as it wet my sandaled toes, but then it rose discreetly to my ankles, to calves, knees, thighs. Chilling, not refreshing.

I kept walking to shore.

Afraid to think. This feeling, this awful feeling, in my gut. Clothed, I walked through the water, my pace slowing with the increasing depths against my legs. That heaving panic rising also in my stomach, afraid to connect with my brain. Too afraid to put words or possibilities on this. Cast iron rolled gold rock solid fear.

I kept walking to shore.

Desperately scanning my horizon for distance. So far, too far. A couple there, along the cliffs. Shielding their eyes to look out at me. Their Labrador, staring. I was too afraid and too far away to shout: 'Help me…I think I'm drowning.'

I kept walking to shore.

The water rose. Thighs to hips. I'm feeling the weight of my clothes now pulling down, my legs getting it harder to push through the eerily lapping water. The sea is giving me its own sinister message: *Shooh, shooh, shooh.* Each movement makes the waves ripple and whisper like backing vocalists on a Supremes track. *Shooh, shooh, shooh.*

I can't swim. Not one stroke. Grew up inland.

I keep walking to shore, the water lapping against my waist and rising, hugging me like a clumsy amorous drunk in a bar. I'm about a hundred yards out. Petrified with what lies ahead of me. The length of it, but more importantly, the depth.

I can't shout to that couple. I just can't. My fear won't let me.

Is this it? Is, this, it?

I keep walking. At least the shore is in sight. My body will be easy to find.

I picture Peter on the water, his terror and lack of faith causing him to founder. I picture Jesus, reaching to him. I don't pray.

I picture the butler in the *Colman's* mustard ad, walking through the water in full regalia with a silver salver pitched high above the waves. On that salver, *Colman's.*

It's a ridiculous ad. It's a ridiculous picture. This is a ridiculous situation.

The fear is hammering within me.

I keep walking to shore, each short step rocking me with the buoyancy of the salt water. I am not sure if the taste of salt on my lips is from tears or from the sea. The water higher than my elbows, rising upwards to shoulders, my arms feel trapped. What if the waves just push me over and I lose my balance? I feel myself on tip-toe, extending my chances, holding aloft my life.

Then it happens with discreet boredom.

The sea stops toying with me.

The water subsides, up to my elbows, my waist, my hips, my thighs. I keep walking into shallower water. Walking to shore.

A gulp in my chest where I'm swallowing fear or inhaling relief. Eventually. I almost can't believe it. Onto the dry.

The rumbling stones of the shoreline under my feet, the crackle of mussel shells. My clothes wringing, the weight of their wetness making me feel as if I'm made of metal.

I clamour onto the rock, my legs shaking, my mind rattling, my heart thumping and my stomach heaving.

The young couple are close, now. They are still staring. Well, naturally they are.

They've obviously put me down for being a few bricks short of a full load or else a heavily over-dressed and very unsexy Ursula Andress. They stare at me and their unwagging, solemn-eyed Labrador stares at me.

And I keep walking with the misplaced dignity of the *Colman's* butler on those shaking legs of mine. Ridiculously imagining a hot mustard foot bath.

Dripping and shaking, thighs chafing, teeth chattering and clothes sopping. Walking the two miles towards my home in Sligo town and away, away, away from shore.

I say the only thing possible to them as I walk past:

'Good afternoon.'

KNOCK

MY MOTHER was a great one for going to Knock.

It was a three hour journey on the pilgrimage bus and she entered into it with the hardiness of a trout. All the night before, she'd have herself busy making our dinner for the next day, airing her shoulder bag, rinsing out her best rain jacket, locating every holy water container in the house, scalding the thermos and making sandwiches—two kinds.

Eventually packing all into the shoulder bag with the finely honed skill of a professional mercenary.

She'd be gone from seven on Sunday morning and we'd nearly be despairing of her coming back by the time we heard Johnny Dolan's wife finally drop her off at the house that night. It could be eleven o'clock or after.

As children, we were so grateful for her return. Our father was a tough nut to talk to and he wasn't much into watching television. What a long old night of waiting and keeping the kettle boiling it was before we'd eventually hear that car turn in at the end of our pass. Humming up to the side of the house, headlights striking through our curtains like the spotlight on 'I Love Lucy.'

She'd land in then, high as a kite, with lots of crackling plastic bags and a clatter of blessed medals that glittered like the scales of a salmon.

A present of some nature for each of us. Our hands itching, we could hardly wait to unwrap the mystery.

Sometimes it was a skipping rope or colouring book. Other times it carried a religious undertone, like a clickedy click key-ring camera that had a slide show of different scenes from Knock when you looked through the view-finder.

The Apparition. The Visionaries. The Gable. The Basilica.

It was written underneath each one what it was and I was mightily impressed.

Other gifts included sticks of seaside pink rock, tooth-breaking and deliciously sweet, it proclaimed 'Eire' all the way through its white sap innards.

Or big thick pencils, a challenge to the strength of the writing hand; with pictures of round towers, leprechauns and all sorts of Irish reminders decorating their carriage. Too big for the average pencil sharpener to tame, this class of writing implement required my father's penknife to lick away the wooden barrel, thus obtain a bum-prickingly sharp nib.

This Knock was a great spot, I figured, if she could go there and bring back such wonderful stuff. She'd even be full of stories about who was on the bus and where they had a cup of tea and who led the singsong coming home.

Oh yes, I thought to myself, *I have a serious liking for this place.*

I could've been nine when I was deemed old enough and 'sensible' enough to go with my father to Knock. I have no idea what sensible meant in my parents minds, but it seemed to carry a lot of weight in their decision-making regarding my social outings.

As a man my father was getting well on in age and the pains had him squeezed tight as the skin on a drum. So this one year anyway, he took a notion about heading to Knock and wouldn't let it go. He wanted someone to go with him on the Diocosen pilgrimage:

to carry his coat and the bag,

to make sure he got the front seat on the bus

and to keep an eye on him that he didn't forget his stick anywhere.

The stick in question was a long-handled one that he got from the Yanks when they were home in August. It had a horse's head carved on the top of it.

God help him, he nearly lost his life when it went missing for three days until it was found in Farrelly's pub where he'd left it the Friday before.

'What were you doing in Farrelly's?' my mother asked him suspiciously, 'you told me you were only going in to the co-op for nails.'

As usual, it was herself who got the bag ready for our Diocesan Sunday and rinsed out our raincoats. She made ham, chicken and salad sandwiches to beat the band.

'Them ones have no tomato, tell him,' she said to me.

I supposed this was the first indication of me being seen as sensible: I could be trusted to remind my father of important information about his sandwich fillings. Already I could see my adult worth creeping in.

He was out of the bed the next morning like an arthritic bullet.

Six o' clock I heard him rattling his knuckles against my bed-room wall:

'Hi! Are you goin' to Knock t'day, are ya? Hi?!'

'Yeah, yeah,' I shouted back at him in a verbal display of next generation lukewarm Marian devotion,

'Yeah, yeah, I'm up, I'm up!'

Well, from the start there was tension.

It was always his way. He'd have himself buried and be back from the graveyard by the time the rest of us would get to his funeral. That's the way he always was. That's the way he was on the day for Knock.

He had to be over at the car park forty five minutes before the bus was due to leave and there was no talking him out of it.

'Those feckers,' he said 'you can't depend on them.' I didn't know who he was talking about. I was more worried about practical things. Which ones were the sandwiches without tomato?

The ones in the *Batch* bread wrapper or the ones in the *Spicers*?

I stared hard through the semi-transparent lunchbox but still couldn't reason it out.

We sat there in the empty car park outside Ballafadda chapel, seven fifteen on an August morning. Steaming up the Ford with two brands of silent resentment.

It was at least another thirty minutes before the headscarved women and sports-jacketed men of the parish started gathering, the way swallows come together on high wires before migrating. One thing became quickly and appallingly clear to me, I was going to be the youngest member of this pilgrimage by at least forty years. This was not the kind of revelation that brought joy to my nine year old heart. The bus landed just two minutes before we were due to leave. That time was eight o' clock sharp on the parish news bulletin and over the holy water font.

Fr Sharkey had even underlined it in wobbly red biro, twice.

I'd always liked that word sharp, it gave time a cutting edge.

'Those feckers,' said my father scowling at the bus driver and at his watch in turn, 'you can't depend on them.'

Right now, he was causing the Widow O' Reilly to wince until I thought her face was going to crack like thin ice on a shallow puddle. She wasn't brought up on that kind of language. She was the very one who'd grass on him to Fr. Sharkey too.

As soon as the doors of the coach opened, he propelled me with his horse's head to the front seat. I must have seemed the most unmannerly pilgrim in Ireland as I pushed through the sea of paisley scarves and sports coats to haul myself on board first.

There was pummelling and jostling as the rest of the faithful equally selfishly tried to get the next best seats at the front.

Fifteen minutes after the sharp departure target of eight am, we were still sitting tight as four dozen eggs in an eggbox, waiting for Patsy Joe Mc Cormick and Wee Aggie the Hop.

'Does anyone know are they comin'?' asked the co-ordinator, as she frowned at us all over her double glazed reading glasses, a list of names in her hand and crystal rosary beads lashed round her right arm like a bicycle lock. This was not a woman to be messed with.

People started firing conflicting information up at her:

I haven't seen him since Sunday, Cissie!

Peter Dan Andy told me he had a turn on the Monday, a flu or some ould thing on his chest...

Thought'n I met him in Walsh's on Tuesday, Cissie, there wasn't a bother on him!

Annie had no mention of it when I met her in the town and that was Thursday, Cissie!'

Oh, she told me she was on for it, and that was Wednesday in the hairdressers, Cissie! Sure she was buying a raincoat.

Then the rebels started, the ones who would've shouted 'Free Barabbas' at the time of Christ's trial.

Go on without them!

Aye, go on!

Sure they're fifteen minutes late, we'll not get into the Basilica for the mass if we lose time!

Aye! Aye! We'll not get the bus parked! We'll not have time for our holy water!

Those feckers, you can't depend on them!

Then, in the distance, a car weaving around Murray's turn.

'Aha!' said Cissie through her reading glasses, 'this looks like Patsy Joe now, isn't that his red car?'

It's him!

It's him alright!

Aye, aye, the job is oxo now!

Oho!

Oho!

And so the rabble fell in with one another again as the red car tediously reversed, shunted forward, reversed, shunted forward and finally scraped itself into parked position alongside the chapel pier.

The missing couple approached, Patsy Joe and wee Aggie. The Hop. Herself with a big hamper and a polka dot full length raincoat with colours so audacious that it would take the plaster off a wall.

Joviality, then as they boarded the coach.

What were you two up to?

Aha, you haven't lost it yet, Patsy, ya boy ya!

You must've been counting all your money under the mattress, Aggie!

Oho!

Oho!

'I had to show young Smith the running of the milking machine,' said Patsy Joe by way of casual explanation, 'am I a bit late? Sure I'm never, wha'? The Man who made time made plenty of it, wha'?'

'We had to turn back for me raincoat,' said Aggie. 'Sure you couldn't go to Knock without a raincoat, but we're still alright for time aren't we?'

'Oh we're grand, we're grand, we're grand, thank God,' shouted the rabble back to them as one hypocritical choral throat.

'In the name of God and His Holy Mother, we're off,' said Cissie, ticking off the last two names and shoving her no nonsense reading glasses into the pocket of her Columbo-style mackintosh.

I wasn't really sure what to expect from a Diocesan Pilgrimage to Knock. One thing that hadn't been forecast was the blitz of rosaries that fell on us as soon as were outside Virginia. Hail Marys and Our Fathers spat out with furious penitent speed from all sides, my father booming louder than the rest.

The bold Cissie leading the herd as she swayed and prayed with a crackling mike up near the engine.

She all but gave us a taste of eternity when she grabbed the bus driver's shoulder roughly on a bad bend near Ballyjamesduff, almost putting him off the road.

And the litanies, the trimmings...the Stars of David, Towers of Ivory and The Comfort of Sinners.

They fell on top of my jarred brain like slates off a roof.

And kept on falling till I thought I'd lose consciousness. Eventually Cissie lashed us all to a halt with a sign of the cross so lavishly applied to her person that it looked as if she were lassoing a wild horse.

But then it was into the singing. The Hail Queens of Heaven and Ave Marias, the Bells of The Angelus and Queens of the May. By this time I had gone into religion overload and was also valiantly trying to fight off motion sickness.

I could feel the bulge in my throat like a rabbit in the neck of a boa constrictor. Hot gaseous discomfort, no sickbag, no respite from the prayer storm. No hope. No rest for the wicked.

Cissie got another rosary out of us before the toilet stop.

At this stage my responses were barely audible. There was a queasiness in my throat and the watery film over my eyes was pure hell. Still I gurgled gamely onwards.

Longford, it was decided, was a great place for a toilet.

'There's that mighty place near the square,' said Cissie to the driver, 'pull up there, Francie, we'll stretch our legs.'

There was an almighty surge of energy when the bus finally pulled up outside the Market Bar, every pilgrim bouncing to his or her feet just as the engine was cutting. My father stalled the lot of them in the manner of Moses and the Dead Sea by putting out his horse's head stick and one arthritic leg and shouting at me to push him out into the aisle. He'd ended it with the appendix 'for feck's sake' just to give his order the quality of competitive urgency that he thought befitting to it.

Poor Jimmy Dan Andy nearly lost his life over the combined hurdle of stick and leg, but in the end had the good grace to haul my father into upright position with me and thus alleviate the potential bottleneck.

I can't remember much about the quality of the toilets, but Longford was a great place for temporarily overcoming the most obvious indications of travel sickness.

There we were, back on the bus, five minutes well up, indeed fifteen minutes well up, waiting for Patsy Joe Mc Cormick yet again.

This time he was lost in action with Jimmy the Nail. Cissie's husband, Big Tommy, was sent on the hunt.

Four pubs were searched before they were finally located. Both sauntered back with their warden casually enough, admir-

ing the window boxes and commenting on all the big cars in
Longford as if the world was waiting on their pleasure.

There was pandemonium down the back of the bus.

*Them fellas know we have to be in the north buspark by half
past twelve! aren't they the gits!*

*Aye! Half twelve, the buck eejits...What time is confessions?
Are we going to miss confessions? Hi, Cissie, what about the
confessions?*

*We'll never get a seat in the Basilica with this carry on. I
want to be at the front for the blessing of the sick...*

*What kind of thirst is on them at this time of day? Now
wouldn't you think the old codgers could wait...go on, Francie!
Go on!*

Thankfully my father had got his obligatory 'those feckers,
you can't depend on them' out of the way by the time the two
defectors boarded the bus, bringing with them the smell of hops
and whiskey and big smiles for all of us.

Oho, the boys!

Yez have all yezzer money spent!

*You're the quare fellas, looking for women to bring
with yez!*

Oho!

Oho!

At least the rabble were back to Triple A strength hypocrisy.

I leaned my head miserably against the shuddering window
and hoped that I'd be able to sleep before the next rosary siege
was announced.

The spire of the Basilica rose like a huge darning needle into the
sky, as if its intention was to prick God in his underbelly and
rouse him into greater consciousness:

*Hey you, hey YOU up there...listen to my prayer, my daugh-
ter has her nursing finals on Monday, my Paddy's operation for
the cancer is this Thursday, Eamon is up for the herd test this
Saturday...help me, hear me...*

The day turned out to be a roaster, damp circles under every arm as raincoats were rolled up with embarrassment and balled into shoulder bags. Prayers and prayers and more prayers, poured into every crack and crevice from aged and youthful lips. I had seen the Grand Prix once on television and I now felt like I was in an alternative go-slow version of one myself. In my situation, the only engines in evidence were the ones that powered the high octance recitation of multiple rosaries as we shuffled at pilgrim pace round and round the old chapel in agonisingly sweltering circuits. The only way we could've gone any slower is if we'd been in reverse.

Verbally, my father belted away on his goatspebble rosary beads with a competitive speed that would leave several more devout believers for dust in his wake. I could tell from his form that his principle interest lay in sitting down on a bench with the sandwiches. I was painfully discovering at first hand that there were several obstacles to be circumnavigated on a day such as this: The fifteen decades, confessions, Stations of the Cross, exposition of the Blessed Sacrament, sandwiches, souvenirs, holy water, mass offerings and the Grand Slam itself : three o' clock Mass in the Basilica. To fail on the acquisition of or participation in any of the above presented a situation so severe that it was obviously tantamount to a samurai warrior having to fall upon his sword with shame. My father was not one to court even the possibility of failure.

'Go on, you,' he poked me with the horse's head as he gave me the three empty holy water containers in the shape of the Virgin Mary and the two Dwans mineral bottles brought along as re-enforcements, 'Go on an' get to that Holy Water tap before them wans have it all gone. Those feckers, you can't...'

I didn't wait for him to finish.

I got it wrong with the sandwiches. He ended up impressing his dentures into a mix of tomato, onion and lettuce.

'What in hell did she put in here?' he asked me with outraged indignation, 'It'd tear the arse out of a feckin' goat.'

When the excitement of the sandwiches had abated, he sent

me off to one of the canopied shops for two large ice creams. He
sat perspiring in a sportscoat garlanded in holy water bottles on
a galvanised bench while I trotted off on my most pleasurable
mission of the day.

My patience in the queue was finally rewarded by two creamy
ninety nines, the cartridges of flaky chocolate giving me the
thumbs up from their ice cream nest as I carried them back in
the manner of an offertory procession to my benched father.

The cones got softer with each step I took under that burning
sun until, in rounded rebellious balls, each molten globe took
a leisurely slide right off their cone pedestal and landed on my
sandalled feet far, far below.

It made me temporarily resemble a clown with giant white
bobble-toed shoes. The chocolate flakes broken-backed and
bleeding to a brown death on the pavement nearby now most
definitely giving me the thumbs down. I fleetingly reprimanded
myself for having bought ice-creams in the shop named after St
Jude. Hopeless case was only a diluted term for what this day
was turning out to be.

What I remember of the run up to the three o' clock Mass
was enough to scar my soul for all eternity. The saintly stewards with their dashing diagonal sashes were not letting anyone into the Basilica until twenty minutes before mass time.
They were very strict on this. Naturally this did not fit in with
my father's lifelong need to be at a place for approximately
an hour before he was meant to be there. When the doors
finally succumbed to the appropriate passage of time, it was
the horse's head treatment again for me as he urged me to get
him a seat at the very front. I did my best. But a steward with
hair growing out of his nostrils told me that I couldn't sit in
the invalid section. I said my father was an invalid and pointed
back to him. And there he was, the newly diagnosed invalid
from Cavan bulling his way at superhuman speed through the
stagnant sea of jostled pilgrims, the horse's head pistoning furiously up and down for all the world as if he were neck and
neck with Shergar in the Grand National. I don't know where

his pains were at that moment in time but he certainly wasn't wearing them.

'You can't sit here, sir,' said the steward, turning his attention to the crimson faced puffing apparition that was my father. 'This area is allocated to the sick.'

'But sure amn't I sick?' said my father to him,' 'I can hardly walk with the pains in me joints. Divil the hair I could move this morning...'

'I'm sorry, sir,' said the steward, 'but this area is reserved for those in need of the Blessing for the Sick and for people in wheelchairs,'

'But sure haven't I as great a need as anyone else?' said my father, 'besides,' he leaned in towards the steward and confided further:

'I have great faith and I've been cured before of many's the thing.'

'Please sir, take your faith to the main body of the church,' said the steward, his face reddening with the effort of dealing with a Christian of this calibre, 'I'm sure God will be able to see you quite clearly from there.'

Then he obligingly helped another steward to propel a heavy wheelchair almost onto my father's gouty right foot.

'Those feckers...' started my father as we processed back towards the spiritual cheap seats at the back.

The remainder of that day blacked out for me. I remember it ending in stony-faced disappointment as I lay in my bed that night. Every time I shut my eyes, I could feel the momentum of being squashed on the bus by my father's bulk or the circular shuffling roundabout of processing around and around the Apparition chapel. All I could hear in my head was the babble of rosaries, like a prayer brook, constantly pouring itself into an ocean for God to wash his feet in. There was no getting away from it. No singsong coming home, either.

The unfairness of life.

Of all the days when people should have been showering money at me left, right and centre for being such a lovely little girl, not a soul had tossed even one fifty pence at me. Not even the price of a stick of rock. Not even out of pity.

And that surely being the day when I deserved it most.

Tweethearts And Funeriddles

THE LARGE LADY in the passenger seat is big into funerals. She scrutinizes every inch of our journey for signs of death. The news bulletin on RTE supplies her with what she needs to go on: A gangland shooting up near Lucan.

It doesn't matter that the gunshot victim is alive and reasonably well in James Connelly hospital. Well enough, in fact, to refuse to cooperate with the gardai in relation to his shooting.

There y'are! squeals my front seat passenger victoriously. *That'll be a funeriddle! We'll know it when the hearse comes, oho! We'll all have to pull in and make the sign of the cross in the name of Jesus, oho!*

The ones in the back pay no heed of her. I have two ladies with Downs Syndrome who appear currently to be in love with each other. They are locked in a life-threatening cuddle in my rear view mirror.

I can hear them in turns,
Ah, tweetheart!
Aww!
Ah, tweetheart!
Awww.
Then one of them says:
Put out the pig! Granny Grunt!

That's me. That's what they call me. They call me that because they love me.

They love me and I love them.

To prove I love them, I shout back to them, 'Aw shut up Droopy Drawers! You too, Mother Goose!'

That's what we call each other when we're on good days.

Another round follows.

Granny Grunt! Go blow up!

Droopy Drawers, pull yourself together!

Mother Goose, you're all honky tonk talk!

The large lady spots a black car coming at us around the bend near the Riverstown junction.

Aha! That'll be the hearse no, oh I'm tellin' you that'll be the start of it now, the funeriddle and the whole lot. Oh shakin' hands at the chapel, that'll be the next thing. Oho it's too late for him, I'm tellin' you, Jesus is the boyo that'll get him! He'd better say his prayers. Aye! It'll be all the Mass cards now, wait'n you'll see. They'll put him down in the ground with the rest of them. Oh that's the end of that boyo!

We are driving toward a heritage fair at ten miles an hour in bumper to bumper panic-fraught traffic. This is a quiet small Irish town we're approaching and I can't see a parking spot anywhere. Cars, vans, people-carriers, horse boxes, jeeps and tractors have all been parked with reckless abandon on both sides of the narrow road. I have barely enough room to avoid snagging side mirrors. My driving capability is seriously stretched.

And my close-range passenger wants to talk about nothing but death.

Now one of my middle row passengers speaks up:

Are we near a toilet? I need to go bad.

Oh dear. Oh dear.

We are not near a toilet. We are just near the bumpers of other cars and total gridlock and my first instance of cardiac arrest whilst in charge of six adults with learning disability in a confined moving vehicle.

Oh now, that'll be the undertaker, do you see him do you

see him! Look! Look! Look! The large lady has spotted a man in a dark suit. I think he's a local politician, but she has higher hopes for him, obviously.

He's the man that'll put him in the box! Wait'n you'll see!
Tweetheart!
Aww, Tweetheart!
Hi, are we near a toilet? I need to go bad...

A guard stops me, big hand up.

Oho! That'll be the guard of honour; he'll show us all the way to the graveyard, you'll see if I'm right, that's what he does. He shows us how to get to the grave, isn't that right, isn't that right.

I roll down my window, harassed.

'You can't go in this way,' he tells me.

He's starting to tell me things about backing up and turning in gateways and driving up three hundreds yards to stewards and yellow signs on the left and it's all going over my head. I'm feeling very, very alone in a crowded place. I know my passengers will start a riot if they have to walk fifty yards, let alone three hundred. Through a field, forget it.

The problem is taken out of my hands.

My big passenger leans over with a huge smile and tells the guard just after he's given me the directions:

That fella has six bullets in him. That's tellin' him. It's no wonder it'll be a big funeriddle, mark my words, oho!

'Sorry?' said the guard, a bit confused.

From the back I hear the shouting:

Ah go blow up, Granny Grunt.
Put out the pig.

By way of explanation I tell him I have a group of friends with special needs travelling with me. They're allergic to walking and the lady in front thinks she's going to the gangland member's funeral, the fellow who was shot in Lucan just today.

'It doesn't matter that he's still alive, she still wants to go to his funeral,' I tell him.

I add on about the lady in the middle needing a toilet and me badly needing a parking space right now. So far the two male passengers are keeping sthum but there's no telling when there'll be a nicotine crisis forthcoming with a bit of foot-stomping.

'I see,' he says slowly, catching the urgency of what's going on. He has a think for a few seconds.

'The best thing you could do is pull up alongside the vintage car display. I'll radio on to the lads to open up the barrier and let you drive in. You'll find a bit of room somewhere in there.'

'Thank you,' I say to the guard and all my passengers wave enthusiastically at him as we bludgeon slowly through a sea of pedestrians towards the vintage vehicle display area.

He smiles in at the lot of us, then shouts over to my front passenger:

'Make sure and say a wee prayer for me after that bucko is buried!'

Indeed' n I will! she declares exultantly, *I can't wait to see them put him down, that's the ould git. Jesus'll show him how to shoot people in Dublin, That's the boy who will!*

True to the guard's word, he has radioed on and our mini bus is flagged through by a grinning steward. He directs me over to a grassy space next to some ancient Morris Minor van. I can't help but break into a smile.

Not only is it black but its reg plate ends with the two letters DI.

It's all too good to be true.

As I cut the engine, my front seat passenger is already blessing herself in anticipation of a damn good funeriddle and even I am starting to enjoy myself.

PLASTIC LADIES

I HAVE ALWAYS BEEN intrigued by the impossible lives of shop mannequins, their frigid plastic nudity, gesticulations and stares at situations they pretend to touch and see. As a child, my memories of the mannequins we had going on in the town were less than attractive.

I remember the ones down in the drapers at the bottom of Main St. Their faces were made of some dubious spongy stuff. It was the colour of American tan tights and it got battered more and more with each wardrobe change. Due to the strange nature of shop window leprosy, some mannequins had lost fingers. Slivers of flesh had been scored from faces, arms and legs. Yet game birds that they were, they kept on displaying the twin sets and the Peter Pan blouses behind the lucozade coloured window. One plastic lady had the misfortune of having her ear attached by yellowing sellotape which sometimes came askew in colder weather, leaving the organ hanging like larvae from the side of her head. Nevertheless, performer that she was, she continued to watch passersby haughtily in the company of her brethren from behind her Clockwork Orange eyelashes.

The upper class boutiques had foxier models altogether, some of them so cool they didn't have facial features at all. Their poises were more dynamic than the drapers' ladies, whose posture seemed arthritic in comparisan. Boutique babes were all set to flounce and swirl, stamp and pirouette. In a way they were the Bailieborough answer to Charlie's Angels, the closest most of us got to glamour in the early eighties. They pushed all life obstacles out of their pout-featured way with their shoulder pads and conical bras or head butted it with their stiff hair-sprayed coiffures. The Draper ladies were old school. In fact they could've been teachers, doctors wives or secretaries, within respected niches of society, content with unchallenged lives where nothing changed ever except seasonally, their clothes. The Boutique Babes were bitches on wheels, waiting for the opportunity to get angsty about something—anything—in their power-hungry feminist lives so they could impale the world with their stilettos and stifle their enemy with their musk-heavy perfumes.

Years later, as art students, we came across a mannequin in a skip. Too good to pass over treasure trove like that, we hauled her out of her shallow grave of broken cabinets, dismantled shop fittings and dinged emulsion tins. The poor thing had been cast out without a stitch. I still remember us bringing her back to our flat, bent over in giggles as we attempted to make the spectacle of carrying a naked life-sized plastic lady down Wine St. look like a dignified affair. Back at our already over-crowded student flat we had to wonder, now that she was in our domestic lives with the nicked traffic cones, stolen pint glasses and pilfered concert posters, what in hell were we going to do with her?

She was christened Greta due to her mystique. I imagine she—like Garbo—would've also wished to be left alone, considering the dubious range of activities we engaged her in. One day we brought her to college and dangled the lower part of her body out the window for a morning, assessing the concern and reaction of passersby. How in general would people respond to the sight of a naked woman crawling in through a barely open window in the middle of Sligo town? Not surprisingly, men seemed to involve themselves more in her dilemma. Only when they got up close and registered our manically grinning faces and flashing cameras on the inside did they smile themselves and walk away faster.

Greta had other outings too. She got to pose with her easel (naked but for wellies and a beret) down by the waters edge, a hog hair paintbrush taped into her right hand. She got to sit (naked but for a woolly hat and an art magazine) on a bench near the river, her tranquillity somewhat disturbed by the two winos who insisted on sitting with her. She enjoyed a swing in the play park. (We clad her for that. The children, you know.) She even had a brief spell as a nudist on Strandhill beach. Before we knew it, end of term came. Time for us to pack up and head away from Sligo for the summer. Not surprisingly, no one wanted to bring Greta home to meet their parents. I certainly couldn't see her having an active and happy life on a Cavan farm. We did the only thing that seemed decent. Went to the nearest skip we knew of. This happened to be outside the mortuary of Sligo General hospital. We buried her in that, under three-wheeled surgical trolleys and other very interesting medical bric a brac. Confident that we had given her the most exciting of life extensions for the past four weeks and that she had known a racy series of adventures that most mannequins can only dream of, we felt that this was the proper place for her to finally be at peace.

GENTLE WHITE LIVES

SHE IS A LADY of indefinable late middle-age.

Her chin has collapsed into several others and under the cor-rugated rubble of skin is the gleaming gold of a heavy chain. She leads a conga of many late middle-aged ladies now entering the coffee shop. It's a coach tour.

Dead giveaway is the dynamic sprint that many of the women encumbered by heavy handbags make towards any architectural possibility that could end in toilets.

The driver of the coach tour comes in with the middle-aged ladies. He is humming in that tuneless way that people some-times do when they don't know what to say to their company but they still need to keep up a show of cheery affability.

They've probably comes to photograph Yeats' bones. They are hobbling, striding, padding.

Retirees, I guess. Many women but few men.

One of these few men is bulging with good humour. He must be already cast as the joker in the party pack throughout this tour. The one to buoy up the spirits with the timely wisecrack, the sing-song, the innuendo and out your other endo.

They are from Manchester.

All soft voices cooing like doves over the Celtic knot work cards, Irish jewellery, and green ceramics.

There is a man in white, completely in white. I picture one

chocolate éclair accident on those impeccable white jeans of his and I shudder internally. He has a beer belly that makes me see him as being more at home in his local pub.

Maybe the *Bell and Whistle* or the *Pig and Bull*, throwing darts and sinking bitter.

From head to toe, he is dressed in this impossible white. His image bizarrely completed by a large white handbag. Its tassellated strap bunched like an untidy rope in his clenched fist.

I'm presuming it belongs to his wife, lost at sea in the Bermuda triangle of the ladies toilets. But I like the fact that he minds it for her, isn't embarrassed. I like the fact also that he and she have come together on this tour, that they can actually bear proximity to each other for the necessary holiday duration.

It must be harder on the men, I always feel. There are only a few of them to so many women. They have to mind their language, open ever so many doors, not curse or belch and always know the answer to everything mechanical that could go wrong with a suitcase, hairdryer, bus air-conditioning and any remote-control operated devices in any given hotel room in the West of Ireland.

I see now that the joker of the party pack has a left arm that hangs suspiciously still.

It is as stiff as the branch of a dead tree and I realise that sometime in his life this man has had a stroke.

From whatever place in his heart, he has come through laughing.

I watch them heave, like a cluster of shuffling emperor penguins, all out through the double doors together. Two of the four men are holding the doors open.

The joker, laughing, the Hero in White giving his wife her handbag as she excitedly fills him in on the nice hand soap and the tiles she's just seen.

Suddenly I am overcome with an enormous waft of affection for them all, enormous.

What have they all already come through in their lives? What have each of these weathered and war-torn retirees survived? What have they celebrated?

They are going on to Donegal. It's a glorious day for it and I am so glad that the Sligo sun shines on them.

For me, the concept of the tour their lives have already brought them on is too much to think about.

Too varied.

Too rough.

Too relentless and long.

Too breathless a view.

I close my notebook on their gentle white lives with a blessing and a wish for their happiness.

Hatpin Horizontal

HATPIN HORIZONTAL is what my mother called her.

It took me until fourth class to differentiate between horizontal and vertical. By that time I realised that my mother had gotten the name wrong but too late now, because it had stuck.

Hatpin Horizontal is the name she gave to old Mrs Brady who lived on the hip of the hill. Mrs. Brady was a wiry cricket of a thing with age-tightened sinews in her neck as taut as the strings on a harp. She dressed like an onion, spring, summer, always.

Layer upon layer keeping her life ticking like a metronome inside her insulated heart. Usually the outermost layer was a housecoat or man's gabardine mac tied round the waist with blue baler twine.

It is possible she was the nosiest woman in the world. Certainly our parish knew none to beat her.

'Tell her nothing,' my mother would warn us at the start of day before we headed down the road to wait for the school bus.

'If she's looking to find out what price daddy got for the heifers, let on you don't know.'

I was quite afraid of Mrs. Brady sometimes. Purely based on the visuals.

She had vampire qualities. Her head would dart out from behind a whin bush next to a roadside gate or maybe up from behind her long grey wall. Always unexpected, even in the expectedness of it. She had that invisibility that magical people seem to possess.

The first indication of a Hatpin Horizontal ambush was when a jaunty grey feather bobbed up from whatever hiding place with a hat, head, shoulders and body beneath it all uncoiling like a loosened spring. She gave the appearance of someone who was mad busy. She might be foostering with twine under the guise of mending a gap in a hedge to stop her cattle breaking out, clipping back some briars, putting a lick of white paint on her gate or gathering a bunch of twigs for the cavernous fire that smouldered constantly in her big dark kitchen.

She always wore the hat. Incongruous though it may have been in the dreary countryside where other women tamed their steel curls with paisley headscarves. For Mrs. Brady, the hat was the signature which announced her. Hard to say now which was worn by who, she by the hat or the hat by her.

It was a brown affair. Maybe once upon a time it was a celebratory item purchased up in Arnott's for a family wedding. It was now the colour of a turf sod, with a fringe of stiff veil latticing her eyes. The feather, solemn and straight, deviated from its rigour to give a tight-lipped curl at the top. This feather bobbed like a conductor's baton as the ambushed conversation escalated to starry heights.

'Yez are home early the day!?'

We'd mumble to this, shuffle our shoes against stones.

'Any slaps?'

We'd mumble to this, twist the strap of a satchel on shoulders.

'Was your daddy in the mart yesterday?'

We'd mumble to this too and not know where to look, start edging forward a bit down the road.

If it was a bad day, she might sidle alongside us for a couple of hundred yards with her hedge clippers and her questions. If we were lucky, we got off with her only keeping pace for a few steps and telling us to make sure and tell our mammy she was asking for her and to come up and see her the next time she was passin' the lane.

We had no time for old women.

And as soon as we got by the Hatpin Horizontal waylay we would snigger and walk faster. Now I think how lonely she must've been, how even the reluctance of our newsless exchange brought some kind of company into her day. Her husband had died just a few years after they got married and she had no children. She lived on her own in that narrow old two-storey house for decades.

Occasionally my mother sent me up to Mrs. Brady's with a home-made brack or a pound of rhubarb jam. Time suspended itself in cobwebbed eternity as I sat at the end of her long kitchen table, fingering the ancient oilcloth. Waiting an age for her kettle to boil on the crane over her three smoky sods. She was extremely economical and tended those sods as if they were meat on a spit, forever tonging them around and about. They resembled the changing faces of a smouldering dolmen.

She was the only person I knew who lived in a house that had the old-fashioned hearth with crane and bellows. There was no magic in it for me. The blue smoke peppered my eyes and conversation was an agonized effort. The resultant tea would be black as tar, served in a chinking cup and saucer, but essentially everything smelling of turf smoke. The smoke shrouded everything in blue mystery. Even the calendar from the butchers in Bailieborough was indistinct. A wall clock chugged faithfully somewhere close by but it was difficult to spot the clock, let alone the time.

I felt I had done a heroic deed for mankind if I managed to spend a whole hour in that dark rank place. The only cheerful aspect of the visit were the diamonds of ochre light cast by the stained glass panels of her front door. They sprinkled the worn boards of her gloomy hall with patches of hope, spilling capricious darts of colour onto the sombre shrug-shouldered coats that queued along the hallway on a row of old-fashioned pegs. Those stained glass droplets were domestic runway lights promising freedom as I advanced, blinking, into the pure daylight with my glad goodbyes; her cold claw pressing my sweaty palm in a scarily tight handshake.

No one was ever able to put an age on her; she was too 'cute' for that. But she lived, it was thought, well into her eighties. A visiting niece found her one day in the yard, where she had fallen after throwing some hay to her cattle.

Unconscious then, she died later down in the hospital. We missed her from the road. She was one life and one light less on a landscape that had little enough going on for it.

After she was gone, the gate at the bottom of her lane was closed.

It got to rusting. The hedges became overgrown and gaped with untended holes and unruly brambles.

Even if there was the ghost of a feathered hat popping up behind them, it would be hard enough to spot.

Suffering Saints

I MUST'VE BEEN ABOUT EIGHT when I decided that I'd be a saint.

It became my worldly ambition.

The promising rustle of the First Holy Communion dress was what started me off. The smell of sanctity oozing from the shiny white prayer book and the precious glitter of the pink glass rosary beads that didn't break when I bit them were additional lures.

I guessed it would be a lot easier for me to be a saint than some of the rest of them in my class because let's face it; I was a better person to start off with. Also, I only had a brother. So fighting over dolls was not an issue in my house. And he had the technical Lego with the wheels and hinges while I had the stuff with the doors and windows and people with roundy yellow heads like pelican crossing signs.

No rows over that, then.

No, thank God, I had it easy enough.

On top of that I had the added bonus of spiritual reading via the *Sacred Heart Messenger* and the *St. Martin de Porres* magazine. The *Messenger* wasn't the most riveting of soul-fodder, but it always had a nice photographic image on the front, often of a family walking in autumnal woods, smiling, a fair percentage of them holding hands. If anyone in my family ever started holding hands it would signal the end of the world. My father said only Nancy boys held hands. I wondered who would call their boys Nancy. Other than that, I envied the *Messenger* family their walk together. We never went walking in our house. We didn't know how to move as a family. The only place we ever sort of walked was the twenty yards from the car into the chapel on Sundays. Even then my mother split for the women's cross-house as soon as she could politely get away from the rest of us and my father usually stopped to talk with some ould fellow who was harrumphing up a jellyfish of phlegm at the side gate.

The *Sacred Heart Messenger* sustained me with its children's page. I liked the riddles and the Spot the Difference pictures. Most of all I liked the kind of visual puzzle where I had to Find The Gardener or some such being who had gone missing somewhere on the page. It meant turning the little magazine around sometimes almost a full revolution before I would spot the missing person lying sideways in a floral arrangement or their nose forming the stumpy branch on a tree or whatever. Even the act of finding that one lost soul made me feel like I was doing my bit to heal the world and ease its pain.

The *St Martin de Porres* magazine had more gristle to chew on. It had characters like Jock Bruce Spider and that little dog who wrote a message to us each month beginning *'dear boys and girls'* and signed it off with *'three barks and a wag of his tail.'* Freddie. That was his name, Freddie.

All in all though, it wasn't the children's page of the St Martin magazine that held my imminent-saintly attention. It was the Thanksgiving page.

So many people wrote in to thank St Martin for all kind of favours granted. As a saint, Martin kept himself busy; curing lumps and bumps that were cancerous, locating lost engagement rings, finding jobs for people who had been out of work for a dreadfully long time, delivering healthy babies, helping nervous women pass their driving tests and causing generous sums of money to appear in financially-challenged houses at just the right time. Indeed, in our house the first thing that was reached for whenever a cow or calf was sick was not the number for the vet but the St Martin relic from my mother's high cupboard. He was an all-round good sort and never idle.

On the strength of his impressive involvement with the common man and his understanding of daily trials and tribulations, I took on to say the Nine Day Novena to him for both a Large Sum of Money and a bicycle. I told him I was in dire need and promised him publication, because understandably he seemed to like a bit of advertising for his good works. Just like a politician who has done great things for his constituents.

I did well for the first three days, and then forgot all about the fourth because that was a Saturday and I always went into town on Saturdays—a huge worldly distraction completely airlifting me from my devout prayer life. By Day Eight I had missed another two days but said the novena on my knees on Day Nine in order to regain lost ground. I also told St Martin that it was quite alright if at this stage he just gave me either the bicycle or the money, whichever he thought was best. But if it was money he was going with, I advised him I would need at least two hundred pounds which would cover both my dire need and the price of a new bicycle from Mc Evoy's. If he was going to plump for the bicycle then could he please not get me one like Kathleen Brady's. Everyone laughed at hers cos of its gawky pink colour and the stupid tassels on the handlebars. If it was all the same with him, I'd like one like Padraig Smyth's—a chopper—only a better-looking one and with more gears for the hills I had to deal with. I figured Martin had his fill of hills in Lima and knew exactly what I was after.

I waited three whole days and never got the money nor the bike. But by that time my thoughts had progressed to holier things. There was a programme on about Padre Pio on RTE One and it showed his stigmata and the way the blood oozed through his mittens and made them look like jam sandwiches and everything. Now I wasn't particularly interested in praying to Padre Pio because all the indications were that he was a bad-tempered enough fellow, but all the same I really wanted the stigmata. That was deadly. It would be a great thing to have at school, to raise my bloodied aerated hand up in the air and say, 'Please teacher, can I go to the bathroom, my stigmata is at me.' And the teacher would bow and scrape and say,

'Yes, of course you can go, dear. Everyone else, close your Irish books and I'll examine you on all the spellings from page 26. *Seas suas gach duine!*'

Oh yes, that would be the business.

But no amount of wishing or staring at my palms would encourage stigmata to gush forth in the way I craved it. Even when I pressed my finger nails hard into each palm the angry crescent didn't stay long enough to give hope. The point of a red biro gave a more authentic embedded circle but it hurt like hell so that was no good either. It seemed that the only way to stigmata would be through a life of devoutness and Good Works dedicated to The Lord. I didn't see any reason why I couldn't pull that one off easily.

So I started straight away.

At home I washed dishes without being asked, I even rinsed out the sugar bowl that held my father's teeth in all their flotsam and jetsam. This counted as a saintly job, right enough. But I stuck with it, even scouring around the scum on the rim with soap pads until I had discoloured the ceramic forever and used half a box of brillo.

I put up with my mothers friends when they came to visit—even Mrs Denning who spat at me every time she talked and on top of that was always going on about how great her Angela was and how the sun shone out of her backend. That was a trial, but I offered it up. I brought in extra turf for the fire without being asked, buckets and scuttles of it, so that it looked like we were set for the Big Chill and there was nearly more in the house than in the turf shed. All during these good deeds of extra kindness and sacrifice to my family I kept my eyes downcast and my expression solemn. I understood that this demeanour went hand in hand with offering it all up. After a few days I heard my father remark to my mother:

'That wan has a horrid puss on her down to the floor. Do you think has she worms?'

My mother claimed she hadn't noticed anything particularly strange about me, which gave me the hump a bit considering that a lot of the sacrifices I had made were meant to make her life easier.

How could she mean it that she didn't notice anything particularly the matter with me? Hadn't I resisted the last slice of cake on the plate at tea-time for the last three days and hadn't I shared my fizz bombs with them all yesterday? Not to mention sweeping out under the stairs on Saturday morning. She must've seen my sanctity in that, surely, because the smell of Skip the greyhound who slept under the stairs would cause even the strongest man to heave.

Well, if my good acts were going to go unnoticed, it seemed that I should cancel out on a few of them and start making more forays to God's house. I was only after First Holy Communion about four or five months so the whole chapel thing was still quite an attraction for me. It might, after all, be the easiest place to become a saint. The problem was, Cross chapel was two whole miles away. That was too far to walk. The hills were murder and St. Martin still hadn't come up trumps with the bicycle. Maybe saints don't answer the prayers of people under the age of eighteen, or maybe St. Martin didn't expect anyone from Cavan, Ireland to be praying to him. Admittedly I had never seen any 'favours granted' letters from Cavan in his magazine. Well, it seemed that the only way I could fit in extra chapel visits was by going with my mother to first Fridays.

She seemed surprised at my intentions of coming with her.

'Do you not want to stop at home with your father and watch that ould detective?'

'No,' I told her resolutely, with all the sweetness and patience that an eight year old saint could muster up:

'I want to go to the chapel and be with my father in heaven.'

'Well, I'll not stop you,' said my mother but she looked at me as if I were a couple of bricks short of a full load.

I didn't want to pull her up on it.

Time enough when she knew how special I was.

All the same she should have understood that being with my father in heaven was a superior choice than being with my earthly one in the kitchen. My earthly father had a tradition of steeping his feet in a basin of water on Friday nights. The smell was pungent and he had horrid blue veins on the tops of his feet that ran all over the place like knotty old twine. He'd cut all the dead skin and calluses off with his penknife and these white flecks snowed all round the basin like a mockery of a halo.

The First Friday took an hour, what with the rosary and the litany and all. I liked the litany. You had to answer 'Pray Puss' to just about everything the old woman with the leaflet called out and I got into the swing of shouting out the response louder than anyone else. My mother threw me a look as if to say: *'I'll make trouble for you when I get you home.'*

I know those looks of hers. Even sainthood wasn't worth it, so I piped down.

I was transfixed by the long stained glass windows behind the altar. When I came to Mass on Sunday mornings they were piercingly colourful. Three lofty figures with crosiers and prayer books and lambs and all sorts, in a marvellous patchwork of glittering glass. But now on this September night even the figures themselves couldn't be seen, let alone the brilliance of their colour. It was like an eerie magic trick. It made it harder to pray when there was nothing to look at but I focussed on the priest and offered it all up. After Mass I made devotional visits to Our Lady, St Patrick and the guttering candle stand, making perfectly angular genuflections at each one. I was converging on a statue of some fellow dressed in brown whose name I didn't know but who had a flower and a kind face when my mother collared me.

'Would you ever hurry on and get out to the car. I want to be home for the news. *Tonight!*'

I told her on the way home that when I grew up I wanted to be a priest.

She snorted with laughter into the steering wheel and nearly put the car off the road at Packie Kelly's turn.

I had heard her say before to some other Holy Mary that a priest in the family was a blessing. Well, this was no way to treat news of an imminent family blessing.

'What put that into your head?'

I wasn't sure whether to trust her or not but I had been thinking heavily on this all during Mass so I figured I'd take the chance and confide.

'Well, they wear nice dresses.'

'Mother of God,' she said and laughed that strange laugh she had when she was the only one who knew the joke. If this was how she took my priestly ambition, it was a good job I hadn't gone the whole hog and told her about my intentions of being a solid gold saint even before I was laid in my grave.

'You'll have to tell your father that when you get home,' she said, 'Make sure and don't forget.'

I knew that this was very important hurdle to get over and I also knew that it would break my father's heart, me being his one daughter and the only one in the house who would polish his shoes and all. But strangely the news caused him to roar out laughing as well. Truly this family of mine was not equipped for such an enormous blessing.

'Jasus!' he said, 'that's a good one. I never thought I'd see the day when I'd have a daughter a priest. If that doesn't beat holy all.'

And he laughed again and then told my sniggering brother to turn on the telly to the right station for the news.

That was the end of it in their minds.

I sat at my end of the table and drew a picture of myself saying Mass, wearing a lovely ruffly dress with crosses and daisies. I emphasised my stigmata with ripping big lines from my brightest red crayon.

Just let them wait, I thought, *just let them wait.*

When my mother had to start buying bandages in town every Saturday for my stigmata and feeling the financial pinch, then she'd sit up and take notice.

Well, I can't say life got better or worse. Certain realisations occurred. The first one being there was no point in doing good deeds in my home if no one else noticed. There were enough jobs to be done without doing extra. And if God saw every little thing like the Catechism said he did, well then he'd see that I pulled my own weight as it was. Besides he had already given me a very hard family to work with and would obviously be keeping that in mind when it came to scoring me on my sanctity.

I maintained a steady course at school and was kind and good and decent to everybody, not that they appreciated, deserved or noticed it.

The idea occurred to me to pull an extra chair in to my table for my guardian angel to sit down on. There was no doubt that my angel would have a lot more duties than anyone else's what with my upcoming sainthood and all. But when Liam Mulligan tripped over the chair coming down from the board and nearly brained himself on the nature table in his projectile fall, Mrs. Brady said to get that chair out of there, it was a danger. She didn't seem to care about the fate of my guardian angel.

'Let him stop at the back of the room like everyone else's,' she said.

I didn't like the idea of my angel sitting on the nature table in a sweaty feathered huddle with all the other common or garden angels, maybe getting his wings wet in the frogspawn or else sitting by mistake on a soggy paper plate of wallpaper paste that someone hadn't tidied away at the sink.

Beyond the fate of my poor angel, however, I was fierce worried around this time about my lack of sin.

Was the Sacrament of Confession not a bit of a waste for me when I didn't sin like everyone else? I agonized over this. Would I have to invent a sin in order to tell the priest something once a month? And then, when I invented a sin, wasn't that a lie and so the next time I went to confession I'd have to tell him that I told a lie. And it wasn't fair because my lie was all about covering up the dreadfully rare fact that I had no sins and if it wasn't for the

Sacrament of Confession I wouldn't be lying at all. I lost sleep over it but didn't dare tell anyone. Holiness was a thing to be suffered in private. I offered it up.

I attended another First Friday with my mother. This time I noticed that the stained glass shone brilliantly from the outside with the lights on in the chapel. But Fr. Kelly didn't have the heat on inside and the church was freezing. All the old women in the crosshouse whispered that it would famish you and they clustered together in their big coats like hens on a roost. The old one with the leaflet gave out the rosary which went on too long in my opinion and the litany made it worse. During Mass Fr. Kelly never stopped either blowing his nose with a loud parping into a giant handkerchief or else coughing his guts up into the sizzling microphone. It struck me that he was always sick and snoddery. Was this something that happened to priests?

It was getting harder. I had enough colds myself without getting extra ones. How would I keep up with the rest of the class if I was off sick all the time? I might fall behind. And me the brightest in the class.

By the time the following First Friday came around, my resolve had weakened considerably. I couldn't bear the thought of going to the cold chapel with the doom and gloom windows and the shivering women in the big herring bone tweed coats and paisley headscarves and sneezy old priest. And especially the really old woman with the frozen hands who sat next to me on the pew reeking of turf smoke and pee and other smells I didn't know but didn't like either.

I decided I'd had enough. Life in many ways on the outside of the chapel was brighter. I'd stop at home with my earthly father and watch a detective where someone gets shot by a greasy-headed creep. My father would bake apples in the Stanley and we'd have them in slurping bowlfuls with lashings of sugar while we watched the detective get his man. By the time my mother would get home we'd have all cleared away and there'd be no evidence to convict us.

So I sat at my end of the table, brow furrowed as I coloured a secular scene of a house with big bright windows and a girl with a chopper bicycle zooming up and down drumlins with a collie after her.

'Are you not comin' with me?' my mother asked me as she struggled into her sheepskin coat.

'No!'

'And are you not still wanting to be a priest?'

'No,' I said curtly and I looked up at her with eyes that were meant to convey heartbreak.

'I'm not cut out for it.'

Though this was probably the saddest news any Irish mother could ever hear, she still went off out the back door laughing.

I bent my head to my secular scene and resolutely coloured any possibility of being a saint right out of my childhood. Time enough to take up the whole saintly ambition thing again when I was a grown-up and life was far less complicated.

CIDONA MAN

OF ALL THE BLIND DATES in all the world, it had to be the worst.

Of all the messed up love lives in all the world he had to walk into mine.

Not that that is how it happened.

After all, he was the one already sitting at the bar with the folded up newspaper and the trench coat. No walking involved. Actually, come to think of it, no love life involved either.

'Excuse me, but are you Declan?' I asked his back in my most falsetto of voices.

My brain was radioactive with nerve endings all clanging together. I was short-circuiting in a heavy mumsy sweater and Dunnes Stores trousers.

Six foot four, his e-mail had told me. But that was hard to judge when he was sitting with his back to me on a bar stool. He could have been one of the seven dwarves on a bender, how was I to know?

He turned slightly in his high seat. Dark hair, framing a face most noticeable for its pallor. Blue eyes, but not the cerulean chips of Paul Newman; a weak mouth that sank into an undetermined chin, a face that that said '*yes*' too much, I figured.

This face paused for an agonizing five seconds before saying 'yes' to me now.

'Yes,' he said, 'I'm Declan. You must be...,' he paused as if trying to recollect, 'Maura?'

'Yes,' I said blithely, laughing as if I had the funniest name in all the world and he was the funniest man in all the world for recalling it.

I threw my bag with casual aplomb on the bar stool to my left and then grabbed the seat of the one in front of me in order to pull it out and sit me and my shaking legs down. Casual efforts not working out, I then started heaving with the Herculean intensity depicted by, say, Spencer Tracy in the Old Man and The Sea.

Declan stared at me, fascinated.

I pulled and jerked the stool for the vital period necessary to establish that I was already well past the criteria for irrational behaviour and now fast approaching the symptoms of demonic possession. And then, then, then I realised that its front legs were wedged behind the foot rail.

Oh my, I said to myself, *Declan, if you have any wit at all, sonny, run now. Run fast, run free, run to the hills for you are surely in the presence of ginormous proportions of human stupidity.*

Declan stayed put, but still stared.

Bad judgement call, Declan, I admonished him internally. *Already I don't respect you.*

By the time I tottered up on the pedestal of my work-out stool, there was what felt like a long-established history of awkwardness between us.

'A drink,' he said.

'Pint of cider,' I said. To hell with the quarter bottles of Chardonnay and lady-like gins and Bacardis and Tia Marias and what have you. I had worked up a glistening layer of sweat and was intent on cooling it down.

'Another Cidona for me,' he said to the dreaming barman, 'and a pint of cider for the...er...lady.'

I'm sitting in Skeff's, Galway with a Cidona man, I said in my horrified internal voice.

Cidona was a drink for childhood memories only. It was not

socially permissible for adults, surely? His accent was English. I asked him where from. He said Middlesex.

I said that was interesting; my mother used to work there, in a bank, I thought.

'Oh,' he said and soon I realised that I'd accidentally let the handbrake off on a conversation that I should've been able to avoid.

'Well, I loved Middlesex.'

And he went on.

'I loved it, really loved Middlesex.'

'Loved it,' he said.

'Left Middlesex and all me mates when I was just a cub of seventeen. Our best nights were Thursdays in the youth club. Me and Bennie and Ron and Colin. Great mates. Brill nights. You don't get youth clubs here with the same atmosphere at all.'

'I cried buckets,' he confided solemnly, 'When I left.'

'Buckets,' he emphasised again and already that weak lower lip of his was trembling with what might dangerously be a portent for another bucketful or at any rate, a gallon.

Well, what he didn't say about his wonderful, all-enhancing Utopian boyhood experience of Middlesex and his good chums Bennie and Ron and Colin wasn't worth hearing. I watched the tidemark on my pint go down, lower, lower, lower...

Conversation not a word to use for this experience as I listened in wretched torpor to the most boring monologue of my life.

If he goes on much longer, I said to myself, *I shall start frothing at the mouth.*

Or else I'll cry buckets, I added as an afterthought.

But now he had advanced from themes of Middlesex to his current work in the HSE service, Galway; where—he told me—everyone loved him and minded him well cos he was a lad from England. Yeah, they all loved him, every single one of them. One of the older women—bless her sweet soul—knitted him an Aran sweater last Christmas.

He nearly cried when he unwrapped it. Buckets.

And he loved them all too, he said.

Particularly Mary down the corridor from him.

He really fancied her. A smashin' gal was Mary. She worked in accounts but had a boyfriend so far as he knew and that was such a pity cos she was the nicest gal he had ever clapped eyes on in this country.

And here he is on a date with yours truly.

I ask you.

And I smiled as I took a last sip from my pint and explained gently to him that I really had to go as I thought my husband was meant to be meeting me at ten past six in Charlie Byrne's bookshop.

I can still feel the weight of his stare.

Guarding The Hood

I was a community arts worker, my life spent coming and going with boxes of art stuff, balls, skittles, toys, big wads of paper. So that's how it started; me landing home one October evening, big box and me, exhausted. I see that Mad Molly's door open.

She's my neighbour in this terrace.

So I get home, and there's her door open. I see my other neighbour Betty hanging her currant bun head out her doorway two houses down in No 6. She's expecting a visitor. The woman with no teeth always visits Betty on a Wednesday. At seven. Just in time to get settled for Coronation St with a cup of tea and some shortbread.

Two hours later I'm going out to my last group of the evening, loaded down with ball, clay, skittles, all that caper. I see that Molly's door is still open. Strange. Very strange, even for her, who surpasses any known interpretations of strange. But I think nothing more of it, go off, do my class, fulfil my role as the non concerned neighbour.

It's quarter past ten. Dark and cold. I'm back at my house, arms loaded with big box of balls, clay, skittles and all. I see that Molly's door is still wide open.

This is the kind of signal that Neighbourhood-Watchers go rubbing their hands in glee over. It's the *'have you noticed something unusual in your neighbourhood'* box marked with a giant green tick.

Yes. Unusual. Check.

So, instead of going to my house, Big Box and me trot down to Betty, the original neighbourhood watchwoman. Ring the bell three times with my elbow.

'Yes?' she says irritably when she answers to me. 'What do you want?'

I tell her it's not so much a question of what I want, but what, in the long term scheme of things, Molly might want. A little bit of investigation. Betty's not inclined to be helpful. She has, after all, been pulled abruptly away from her scintillating conversation with the woman with no teeth. They've probably been interrupted from their critiquing of last weeks Late Late Show and who does Pat Kenny think he is cos he'll never be Gaybo and them ones doing the Riverdance had hardly any skirts on them and why does no one remember the great man Bishop Casey was and all that jazz.

In fact, even now, I can hear the woman with no teeth lowing softly from inside No. 6:—'Who dah a' da doo' Behhy? Who id ih a dis houh op da nigh'? Behhy? Who dah? Hah? Who da?'

'Well did you ring her bell?' Betty asked me impatiently.

I told her that no, I have never rang Molly's bell.

'We're going into this together,' I firmly tell her.

'Come on then,' she said back to me.

'Be back in a minute, Agnes!' she bellowed into the toothless visitor who was still cooing the great question of her life this night :- 'who dah? Behhy? Behhy? Who dah?'

For some reason, as I carried my box back towards Molly's house, Betty thought it fitting that she should take a pink ball from the top. Holding it under one arm like a GAA All-Star, she plunged her finger on the bell of No. 5 with an Angel Gabriel *Oh Hail Molly Have I Got News For You* kind of determination. No sooner had she taken her fleshy digit away than she leaned on one portly leg into the house like an overweight ballerina and shouted merrily, 'Yoo Hoo Molly? You Hoo! Molly! Aw you they-ah?'

'Yoo Hoo, Molly, aw you they-ah? I say Mol-eeeee! Aw you they-awwwww???!'

No answer. And believe me, it would've taken a dead, desperately comatose or already decomposed woman to have ignored Betty's booming Dublinese tones.

'Something's not right,' I said quite unnecessarily to Betty. In my head I was thinking to myself: don't we look like a pair of big buck eejits standing here anyway? For all the world, if Molly DID come to her door, it would look as if the two of us wanted to lure her by clandestine means to some dark uninhabited place under the guise of wanting to play: *Oh Molly come out, it's a quarter past ten and its your two mad neighbours here. Do let's play! That's right! Nothing at all unnatural about our behaviour! Don't be suspicious of a single thing. Let's go play with our big pink ball and box of cheap skittles...aw c'mon Molly, yer no fun...*

Betty was inclined to agree with me on the 'something's not right' theory but being a Dubliner by trade, breeding and unfortunate genetics she was savvy in her style of hysteria.

'We'll not go in,' she said, demonstrating this inches thick savvy.

'—Because if anything goes missing ever on her inside, the ould yoke'll blame us.'

Meanwhile I'm thinking over and over again: *she's dead! Betty, she's dead! she'll not be missing anything but her circulation!*

'We'll ring her,' said Betty then and in a bulky bustling movement which did not brook arguing with, she was already stamping her way back to her own house. I was hard put upon to follow the good ship Betsy but made it in her front door in time to hear the woman with no teeth asking her:

Wha' goin' on Behhy? Who dah ou theah? Wha' goin' on, Behhy?

'She's residential,' I tell Betty, 'Not golden pages. The other book, the blue one.'

The woman with no teeth is mashing tea from a china cup and is mightily interested in what we're about. We find Molly's number.

'Here you ring it, young wan. You saw the door open.'

Dublin courage, not much to be said for it.

She calls out the number to me slowly, scowling through reading glasses: *oh seven one oh no, you don't need that bit do you six three oh five oh wait is that another three five oh I think try that. Oh no, hang on that's Matty Brennan, I think, not Molly...Would she be under the husband's name I wonder now...*

The second attempt gets us through to Molly's number. I am reeling through words in my head, what do you SAY to someone in a situation like this?

Oh ah hello Molly, is it yourself that's in it? we're just here in Betty's ringing you because we thought you were dead....Not a bother on us, Molly, not in the least, Oh hang on Molly, gotta go, Betty's just spotted another pig flying through her living room and she wants me to take a belt a it with the fly swatter. Well sure, bye for now, cheery bye, bye byeee!

But there was no answer. That phone rang and rang and rang, me tentatively looking into it, listening into it, holding nervously on to it for all that time. Betty glaring through her spectacles.

'No answer,' I said to her, making the mental note that I tended to say a lot of unnecessary things to people. But it seemingly isn't unnecessary info to the woman with no teeth.

Id theah no anthah wih Moweee? Id theah noh?no antha on da phone? Oh my oh my now, wha wong wid Moweee? Wha' wong theah?

'Go out and see is her light on, out the back,' Betty commanded me.

'Or maybe I should call the guards?' she said then, showing uncharacteristic indecisiveness.

'No, wait until I check out the back,' I said.

I didn't want her getting all trigger-happy about ringing the guards. Betty, you see, had a succession of cars crashed into, stolen, joy ridden and burnt out. She was a known figure to the local constabulary.

They probably had a phone that flashed with a nuclear red light whenever she rang in to the station in Sligo town. Whoever answered the phone to her up in Barracks street probably got Good Ole Garda of the Month award and a bottle of Blue Nun for the missus.

There's only one thing for it: I go to my yard and haul away at the ladder that's been incumbent against my exterior wall for the last six months. Something to do with my hopes of painting the drainpipe. Now Riley my dozy spaniel comes to life in his tenement basket in the scullery. He sets up an unmerciful yowling and sangfroid barking fit to wake the dead. I grimly wonder if that's what he is doing, as I arse and twist with the ladder. I pretend I'm putting it up against Betty's wall, just in case Molly comes out unexpectedly and catches me looking furtive. So, I stand halfways up the ladder outside Betty's house feigning painting the wall with a phantom paintbrush until I come conscious of what I'm doing and grimly realise that to all intent and purposes anyone looking at me would be quite justified in thinking I'm not right either.

But there's nobody looking.

Down I shamble, haul the ladder little by little towards Molly's wicket door. This is the scary bit: placing it square against her wall and making the ascent.

It's a case of step by step.

Step by step up, step by tremouring step. And then. Like those humpty dumpty cartoon drawings we all did at school, I peer over the top of her yard wall, my hands splayed out to left and right of my big harmless face. Oh dear Jesus, just don't let her be looking out the window.

There's a light on!

The curtains are pulled partways, but still a good section of Molly's living room is exposed like a stage setting. I register the flickering blue light of a TV screen in the left corner. Not that I have to depend on the visuals. Even out here, it's booming away—some bloody current affairs programme, no wonder the woman couldn't hear a doorbell over THAT racket.

But Molly?

I scan the stage.

Is it my imagination or is that a hand on the wing of an arm-chair to the very right, almost out of sight?

I crane my neck, but it's no use. I can't be sure from this vantage point.

Got to go down the ladder, step by tremouring step and move it a little more left so's I can peer to the right of this living stage.

Tremouring step by step up...

It's her!

I had never looked on sudden death before but held no doubt in my mind that I was looking upon it now.

I felt sick to my stomach.

There she was. Poor Molly, That was her gnarled hand, white as death. She was sprawled in her armchair, her face as pale as a damask tablecloth, thrust backwards in an unnatural position, her mouth wide open in a terrifying rictus, eyes closed in what might be everlasting peace.

Well, peace maybe but not as we know it, Jim.

Those alabaster hands were almost eating into her chair with a supernatural grip. Had she suffered much, poor Molly? The man on the blue current affairs programme couldn't tell me, but he kept insisting on giving out to her about the ridiculous costs of bin charges in North Dublin and how did the corpora-tion expect the average family to cope?

Step by tremouring step, down.

In I go to Betty.

'Well?' she scowls. 'Is she in there, is she?'

'Yes,' I say, softly,

'Betty, it's time to call the guards.'

'Oh no,' says Betty. 'Is she...???'

'Think so. Call them.'

'Poo' Mowwheee, poo poo Mowwheee!'

Betty said *yes guard, it's me guard, the lady in No. 6 St.*

Martin Terrace in Glenboy. Smyth. Smyth with a 'y'. Yes, you know me, guard.

'I'm concerned about a neighbour,' Mrs Smyth with a 'y' told him, 'a Mrs Brennan in Number 5. That's correct guard, Brennan, Yes, Number 5 St. Martin's Terrace, that's correct guard, very concerned. I am, yes.'

After being in conversation with her for barely a minute he told her he'd be out with another fella in ten minutes.

Yes guard.

Thank you, guard.

Twenty past ten on a chilly October night, Betty shooed myself and the Woman with no teeth out to the cupboard in her hall until she'd gotten us each a coat to wear while waiting for The Authorities. She had a trench coat of indeterminate cleanliness which she forced upon T.L.W.N.T., that lady being of even smaller stature than Betty. The hemline completely encased her feet and made her look like a faulty dalisk from the Dr Who series.

I worked out even unluckier. I got the brown sheepskin. Made me look like Paul Glazier at his surliest best during the Starskey and Hutch years. Betty herself just did the Columbo meets The Pink Panther with her beige lengthy trench coat and sheepskin gloves.

Then followed the longest part of the evening.

Waiting for a Garda's estimation of ten minutes to go by.

We stood on the pavement outside Betty's front door, The Three Columbo sisters. There was a certain smugness to our stance as we shuffled around self-importantly for the first five minutes, like a trio of Onlookers waiting for the RTE television crew to arrive On The Scene. But basically, we had the look and attitude of 'We Saw It First And Raised the Alarm Like the Good Quick-Thinking Public-Spirited People We Are' gloating quality to us. Then it started.

'Is that them?' from Betty.

'No Betty, that's a motorbike.'

She was twirling her head like one of those jumpy stupid toy dogs that people often choose to have in the rear windows of their cars.

She scowled up towards the football grounds.

'Is that them now?'

'No, Betty, that's a tractor.'

Another noise, from Park Road this time. She raised her nose to the wind like a tracker dog.

'Is that them now?'

'No, Betty, that's a Tesco articulated lorry. Look, would ya, you can see the writing on the side from half a mile away. T_E_S_C_O.'

'Don't be so smart, young wan.'

'Poo Mowwheee.'

Well, thank God the woman with no teeth brought us back to the purpose for us waiting here, spinning on our heels and nodding self-importantly at every curious pedestrian who passed us.

'Is that them now?'

That's a friggin' hearse, ya fruitcake.'

'Oh God bleth uth and sabe uth!'

'Is it one of Foleys' or Feehily's?' asked Betty.

'Betty!'

It must've been at least half an hour when I finally saw the squad car coming.

No flashing cherry, no screeching of brakes, no urgency on any level. Taking their time, the passenger rested his elbow casually on the door frame as his buddy puttered along. For all the world like they were Sunday driving and cooling a bag of chips simultaneously. The guards could not miss the Death Squad Trio congregated in burlesque bundle on Betty's doorstep. Driving guard slowed down even more so's his passenger could casually call out.

'Any of you the woman who rang in a while ago to the station, are yez?'

'Yes guard, that was me, guard, we're concerned about...'

'Right y'are. We'll go down and turn, so, see if we get a spot to park her. Grand evening, thank God!'

Off they cruised, nice happy relaxed but a bit ambivalent-to-adventure gardai, not much interested in Betty's concern. We forlornly watched their tail-lights do a gentle samba on the roundabout before tootling back into our lives. It took them almost five minutes to be happy with where they'd placed the car and how they'd parked her, get out of it, hitch up their trousers, jingle the loose change in their pockets and adjust the tightness of their radios. I never knew there was as much decorum entailed in being a guard.

They didn't introduce themselves, so I still have to refer to them as Guard One and Guard Two.

'So yez are a bit worried about yer neighbour,' said Guard One, hitting the nail on the head.

'Yes, Guard, That's correct, Guard.'

Betty fills the guards in on Molly's open door situation and how it's never open like that and how unusual it is that it should be open for so long, guard, and that we're all Very Concerned.

'Well, did any yez go in to check up on her?' asked lugubrious Guard Two.

'Eh, well no, not exactly, guard,' said Betty.

'None of yez?!'

'Eh well, no, guard, no, that's correct.'

Guard One and Guard Two looked at the Death Squad Trio like we were a triple pack of wittering idiots.

'You see guard, we were afraid to go in because if anything in yon one's house went missing afterwards or got damaged she'd put the blame on us.'

'Right so,' said Guard Two, 'sure we'll go and check her out anyway.'

Off they amble towards Number 5. It's one press of the door bell and in they go.

There we are again. The macabre version of the Andrews Sisters. Waiting anxiously for our Boogie Woogie bugle boys from Company B to return and give us the low down.

Poo Mowwheee. God lub her, she's pwobabwee in heaven,
said the woman with no teeth, waxing all affectionate.

I found myself praying a prayer that I have never prayed for
any other human in my life.

*Please let her be dead. Oh please Lord, please, please let her
be dead!*

You see, it was beginning to rankle with me that it was my
sighting of Molly—deathly pale, gnarled hand, slack-jawed and
all that caper—that had inspired me to get Betty hopping on
the phone to the gardaí. Now what if she wasn't dead? Oh God
no, she had to be dead, she simply had to be. Or unconscious or
something nice and justifiable like that. I mean, the screaming
racket of that TV! Please Lord, we're looking for death here or
a bad heart attack at the very least.

Those guards were taking an age. An absolute eternity. We
revolved on our nervous heels on Betty's doorstep. Betty getting
impatient by turns: '*Would they ever hurry on! What's keeping
them?*' But that interspersed with: '*we were concerned about
Mrs Brennan there in Number 5. We called the guards ourselves. Her door's been open all evening. We're very concerned.
Very,*' to any passer-by who seemed remotely curious about the
presence of the squad car or indeed our melancholy personas
gathered at a front door at that late hour.

Guard Number One emerged, his portly form moving slowly.
I registered his measured steps coming towards us as Guard
Number Two also came out to the front of Molly's door and
leaned in towards it again, his face the picture of gloom. He
stretched one hand up against the wall and I couldn't be sure
in the dark if he was reaching for his radio with the other. He
certainly looked like he was dealing with the heaviest situation
this day had so far offered him.

She's dead! I crowed cheerfully in my mind. She's dead! She's
dead! She's dead!

Guard Number One kept coming towards us. Those slow
measured footsteps.

Now I could see his facial expression. Not a happy one.

Not, one could say, relaxed.

She's dead, then, I said in my head. Thank you Lord, she's dead, she's dead, she's dead.

And then he was beside us and I'm watching him and I'm watching Guard Two at the same time who may or may not be on his radio and it's like everything happened at once. The most devastating words I have ever heard about a neighbour. They came from the parched lips of Guard Number One.

'She was asleep!'

That's what he said.

She was asleep!!!

Then I became more aware of Garda Number Two and why he was looking so woebegone. It was because he was listening to Molly. That's why he's leaning against the door jamb. There was her head bobbing up and down at the door, now that I looked hard at it. I could hear her voice shrill with laughter:

'Sure I thought yez were the tilers! Wasn't I waiting all day for them to come? That bathroom is a holy living dread round the toilet and I had these fellas told to come today. Sure I thought yez were the tilers! Sure yez took a right hop at me, so yez did, comin' in on me like that. There yez are, now. I was doing the varnishing there in the hall—what do you think of that colour now, isn't it nice against the stand? But the bloody ould smell of the stuff must've knocked me out when I went in to sit down after the salad. I do like a salad for the tea nothing too heavy it does give me heartburn if I eat a big fry up in the evening but now I don't like tomatoes they give me wind so they...'

Her voice trailed off momentarily when she saw us still standing outside Betty's.

'Good evening, ladies!' she called out heartily.

'I thought these boys were the tilers! Didn't I get a land when I woke up with one of them poking me and I get a grab of him because, sure, I don't know where I am with that bloody varnish—it's a holy dread so it is—the one with the free brush— and I sez to the lads here, are youse the tilers, are yez? And then I see the stripes on that fella's jumper, and I sez—cute enough of me—youse wouldn't happen to be guards now, by any chance?! Hah, wasn't that a good one! Youse wouldn't happen to be guards!'

Everyone bottle-necked to the exits.

Guards, neighbours and all shambled off the stage as quickly as possible. The Columbo trio tripping over ourselves to get back into Betty's. We left our coats back at her dodgy wardrobe dept in the hall and then collapsed laughing.

It was, after all, the funniest most temporary death to happen in Glenboy. Even in our mad, mad world.

Cows

I MET A WOMAN in a green van who was missing a cow.

In the narrowness of the country road she asked me from the window, fluffy hair framed by jammy-faced children.

'Have you seen a cow?'

I said no.

Not sure if it was a lie because in my life I have seen many cows.

Off she flew, upward thrust of confetti gravel spraying the air as she sped away to spend her Saturday zigzagging the roads of Farnaharpy for a cow. Illogically I continued my walk looking into ditches, drains and frog spawned rivers with extra attention as if somehow, against incredible odds, I was the one who would win today's Spot the Cow contest.

In my life I have seen many cows.

Loved the warm pleated accordion folds of their necks as they swivelled their heads in the byre. Eyes with Hollywood eyelashes. Those eyes, oh those eyes, so big, soulful and brown.

I have seen cows milked, seen them calved, seen them graze and even seen them shot before my eyes and reeled up by their hooves onto a factory trailer like a huge catch from the sea.

Most of all, I have seen cows in community, solid teeth rip-grazing a field methodically, tails switching, flesh rippling against the irritation of summer flies.

Solid hooves lifting and clumping down again on firm after grass. Lying in the middle of a field in good weather, close to the edge in bad.

Bovine black and white jig saw pieces were the barometer of weather, as well as being our farmyard clock. They knew milking time better than we did. They gathered at the gate morning and evening like devotees at a rock concert hoping to catch a glimpse of their hero. They belched and chewed, lowed and bellowed until they did. In most cases, they settled for the burr-coated collie slinking low to the ground, or the putter putter advance of their Lord and Master on the Massey 35.

I can remember the lowing they made, some strident, some melodic, their personalities coming out in who would be the one to start a head butting contest or lock horns with an old adversary. Our herd leader was a crotchety old Charlaois. She was as thin as a bag of bones yet she point blank refused to let any other cow walk in front of her in the undulating procession to or from the milking ceremony. She was the Queen of the Head Butts.

We had names on every single cow, from the pretty names like Baby Doll, Girlie and Shirley to the ones that were named after the farmers from whom heifers were once bought; Old Bell, Black George, and Big Brady. In the end, as our herd got bigger, my mother resorted to calling cows in a certain dynasty Splot One, Splot Two and Splot Three, which indicated the generational relationship linking them. It was the Cavan bovine version of The Godfather.

The cows and creamery cheque were our livelihood.

Milk was the warm white life's blood of our growing years.

I sensed it through the glass vats and tubes in the dairy parlour. The utter importance, the vitality in every way. I loved to put my hands on those vats, feel the comforting warmth in winter, inhale the sweet aroma of fresh milk being pumped, filtered and piped into the two hundred gallon tank. Minnie the Mog was the long-serving farmyard cat who took up her place on a torn bag of hard cement in the dairy corner. She coiled her paws compactly beneath her as she waited till the end of milking when she would reap the rewards of a creamery can lid of warm milk. Her kittens seasonally jetting back and forth from hayshed to dairy to check on the progress report. She batted them off with a hiss or a stabbing paw. She knew the waiting game and taught it to them too.

Cows were everything.

From the moment they wriggled out into life as a glistening heifer calf onto a bed of sharp golden straw to the moment they were retired out to the factory or Ballyjamesduff mart, cows were absolutely everything on a dairy farm.

They were the first reason to get up every morning.

They were the reason to be there every evening.

They were the routine that could never be broken.

They were the incomings and out-goings.

They were the reason we could never take a family holiday.

They were the money for winter coats, new shoes.

They were the love and the hate, the ups and the downs.

They were the resentment and the gratitude.

They were the rhythm of life itself.

I look deeper into the hedgerows and hope that woman in the green van finds her cow. I think I realise the importance of what she is missing.

Wasp At The Window

I caught the bus on O' Connell St. The 14A.

That old woman. Frail as a bent twig, Dancing around the Floozie[1].

A big. No, not just big. A *gigantic* cross in her arms.

Singing about Jesus. All dressed in black.

'Jeeee-susss,' she sings, 'Jeee-susss.'

Sings it like it's got a whole heap of syllables in it; a word that should only take a second to say, she makes it last for ten or more.

She gave me the creeps when she got on the same bus as me.

The driver took the fare without looking at my face. All my money was sweaty and I was slow and clumsy. The Jesus woman's cross dug into me from behind. All the other passengers veering away from her like sea whitethorns, not willing to come into contact with her or her Jesus.

I leaned my head against the window and shut my eyes as the bus juddered and rattled its way towards Merrion Square, Rathmines, Highfield Road, then my stop.

St Luke's Hospital.

I never brought grapes.

---

1   The Floozie in the Jacuzzi was the informal name for a sculpture piece that existed for some time in O'Connell St, Dublin.

Sometimes I brought hand cream. She liked *Atrixo*. It wasn't greasy.

Or a magazine, something like the *Ireland's Own* or *Woman's Way*.

Or any kind of a one with Gay Byrne on the cover. She liked him.

It was impossible to know what to really bring. I felt like everyone on the bus always stared and broke into silence as I got off the 14A. It's like everybody knows the ultimate destination of that stop on Highfield Road.

I walk in tar-sticky heat up the beautiful avenue to St. Luke's main entrance. My anonymous chiffling plastic bag swings from my right hand. I can feel circular patches of damp under my arms. Everything around me is so serene and immaculate. So nipped and tucked and hospital-cornered. All the pain neatly folded away on the inside. The panes of the long windows gleaming out. Wards and wards of different family stories.

Her bed was the one next to the window. On the right as you went in. I was so glad to have that window. It gave me something legitimate to stare out at when the tears pricked my eyes. Every weekend I came up she was getting thinner. A distended bump under the mattress indicated the fluid retained due to the secondaries now in her liver. The swelling expectancy. The unavoidability of what was to come. They had told me the week before that what they were looking at now was 'quality of life' and pain control. There was no point in causing her any further distress with operations that would not be successful. They had white coats and clicking ball points. I had a dry mouth and a fixation on a spider plant drooping from a filing cabinet. How could it look so green, so far away from the light?

It turned out that the spider plant wasn't real. Even though it had shoots dangling from it that looked like new life.

I checked it when they left me alone to cry.

She doesn't appear to be in any distress, they told me. She is comfortable.

I squeak into the ward in my *Dunnes Stores* runners. I know I am making faces at the noise I am dragging in with each footstep.

She is asleep on this sunny Dublin day, her face turned on its right cheek, sleeping on her palm as I have seen her so many times.

She does indeed seem comfortable. They have not been lying.

I sit in the chair that's sandwiched between the wash hand basin and a tall waste bin, a commode, a suitcase and a walking frame. It's like a bizarre bring and buy sale. I hear the buzzing of an insect hopping against the window behind me as I stare at her sleeping face and sketch it into my pad. I do not know how long she will sleep or whether she will even wake up before I leave. I will not wake her.

My sketching is a way of being with her, of knowing her in a way I have never had the chance to before, of seeing and caressing the details of her face that I never properly got the chance to notice in all the movement of regular life.

There are the trappings beside her on the bedside locker.

The tall anonymous water jug.

The squat glass.

The box of *Kleenex* handkerchieves.

The Connemara marble rosary beads.

The kidney-shaped stainless steel dish.

I sketch their outlines into her picture. The rails of the no-nonsense hospital bed, all the mass-bouquets strung out like nappies on a line across the top. And also—like Christ on the cross—on the very top, where names are supposed to go, is her name.

Her first name in full, Josephine.

Not the name by which she was known by real people in her own real world, Josie. Josephine was the name of an emperor's wife. It was historical, tragic, removed. Not *her*.

I see the shaping of three pillows indicating the attentive care the nurses have put into her comfort. The pillows cradle her face in its slumber. Her cheekbones are so sharp. They emphasize the hollow of the sunken cheek. I have to lean harder on my pencil to get the tone right.

I swallow.

The curl is gone from her hair but still that aristocratic nose, that hasn't changed.

That part is easy. I draw it without looking.

Long elegant fingers, but thinner, under her face. No wedding ring, won't fit. This is too hard. I stop.

I hear her groaning as she stirs. Moments later, the groggy awakeness. She focuses on me after a little while and tries to clear her throat in order to say that word which is a lie and a greeting. The way we say hello in our family.

'Well,' she says.

'Well,' I say back.

It is hard to know what to say when neither of us can speak the truth.

She asks me about the journey from Sligo. I make up something about a drunk getting on in Carrick and how the driver had to put him off at the side of the road in Jamestown because he wouldn't leave a woman alone. I used lots of exaggerated description about smell and curses and how it took the strength of two other male passengers to help the driver dislodge him. Not a word of it was true. The journey had whined along in the usual fashion for three and a half uneventful hours. The fleeting hedges winding me in towards my destination like a skein of sickly but persistent green wool.

I told her about my dog back at home and how he's been caught red-pawed chasing my neighbour's cat. He was caught because he was stupid enough to stay at the scene of the crime under the tree barking up at the cat as it hissed down at him. Our neighbour came out with a big saucepan of water which finally got rid of the dog. When he came back home soaking we knew he'd been up to some mischief but didn't know the exact nature of it until the same neighbour came up to our house later and gave out yards about our animal's behaviour and how he could be put down for his viciousness.

Not a word of it was true.

We don't have a neighbour on our lane.

I don't even know anyone who has a cat.

But she listens and smiles and says,

'Isn't he the right git, that old dog? What did you name him again, Brady was it?'

'Riley,' I say.

'Reilly,' she says.

'That's meant to be Riley Ace of Spies, not Reilly as in Cavan,' I tell her, as if that will make any difference regarding the temperament of our Springer spaniel or how we pronounce his name.

The buzzing persists at the window. I look behind me to see what fly is trapped, just to give my eyes a rest from what is facing me.

It's a wasp. His amber and black body flinging and fizzing up and down the pane as he looks for a way out of this imprisonment. Out into the clear green world of St. Luke's lawns and further to the buzz and rattle of Dublin city centre. The grit and grime, sun and bustle of ordinary life. It's glorious out there.

'What's that at the window?' she asks.

'It's a wasp,' I tell her.

'Let him out.'

I really want to.

I know that this dark world of patients, soft tip-tope visitors and seamlessly efficient nursing staff is not his place. Not his life. But it's so hard to get to the window with the commode and the frame and the slippers and chair and...everything.

'Would you ring for the nurse,' she asks me then, groggy, trying to swallow.

'I need to sit up.'

I ring the bell and am amazed at the speed at which a white uniformed figure is discreetly beside the bed.

'The dish, is it, Josephine?'

'Mmmn,' she says.

In an expert moment, the nurse has my mother propped up in a position where she can vomit into the crescent dish.

She is exhausted now. The nurse arranges the pillow for sleep. My mother, with her eyes closed says, 'Jesus.' Over and over. '*Jesus. Jesus.*'

The tears prick my eyes and I turn to the window. Hearing that wasp battering his brains against the transparency of his pane.

My father arrives half an hour after. She is sleeping again.

I hear him coming in, the shuffle of his slow feet, the rhythmic clack of his stick. A loud cheerful word for the pretty young nurse from Waterford.

He is not afraid to make an entrance. Even in the corridor I can hear him saying how the traffic was a huare and how they didn't have time to stop for a bite to ate or even a sandwich. His stomach thinks his throat's been cut. He could eat the hind leg of the Lamb of God, he tells her, and come back for the Sacred Heart. I hear the nurse laughing and telling him she'll bring him in a cup of tea and a few biscuits. He's loud in his thanks.

When he sees me at the bedside, he asks me how she's doing today.

I say, 'well.'

He's not able to accept any other answers. He bends his arthritic body towards the bed and strokes back the grey hair from her forehead with his huge thumb. I wish I could have done that, I say to myself. *I wish I could've done that.*

'Poor Josie,' he says then, 'God love you.'

He swivels around then almost with anger from the bed. I get up from the chair and pull it a little bit closer for him.

'What's that huare doin' in here?' he asks before he angles for the chair.

'troth'n I'll deal with that boyo!'

He reaches out his walking stick directly at the window and with a steadier hand than I would've credited him with at his age, squashes the feruled end of his stick directly upon the form of the wasp. There is a slight wet stain on the glass. The wasp's body now a distorted shape on the window sill.

The next afternoon I return to Sligo. As I shoulder my rucksack in through the door of our cottage, Riley is going mad with excitement.

He wants to show me all the torn slippers and sticks he has accumulated since I left yesterday morning. My friend puts on the kettle and asks me over her shoulder how everything is up at the hospital.

I turn to look out our open front door and I say, 'well enough,' as I stare down at the glittering waves of Lissadell on the horizon.

Just outside, the fushcia is having its blood red pulse monitored by the electric fence. If we're really still, we can hear it tick from the room here. The wasps are flying in their droves all around and through the fushcia. It is wasp heaven, if ever there was. Sheep are blobbing the rushy fields and the trees have the fragile transparency of their early summer dress. Flies zip in and out through our open doorway. I think back to the hospital wasp again and I can't believe I am losing my mother.

This is a different world, humming and buzzing with life. This is *my* life.

I put my mug of fresh tea on top of the television and I get down on my knees to clasp the hopeful spaniel's black silken ears between both hands. His eyes are brown and bursting with love and enthusiasm. His nose glistens with moisture and is brittle at the edges with caked clay. I can see his nostrils whistle in and out. He can't breathe through his mouth too well because he's got half an Action Man torso rammed into it.

My friend sees me looking at it.

'Don't ask me,' she says. 'I think he found it in the turf shed.'

Poor Action Man is flailing his limbs for release. The dog's breath stinks. He's got brambles velcroed to his chest. I look at him; really see him, this Riley Ace of Spaniel Spies, not Reilly-from-Cavan. Persecutor of phantom cats. I move my hands to tear off the bramble and feel the ecstatic thump of his heart. He drops the very sticky Action Man at my knees as a sacrificial offering and jumps at me, his paws on my shoulder as he gives my face a huge salivated lick. I grab him in a bear hug and I say into his fur:

'You know something, you stupid, hairy, smelly, conniving old git?'

And I push him back a bit from me as I look into his delighted brown eyes:

'I love you!'

I ruffle his long soft ears and pull him back into the body hug again. Every inch of him is trembling. He sighs rapturously into my ear. I kiss the top of his head, I feel the sting of tears in my eyes and I am laughing and crying at the same time.

But they are good tears. They wash away the transparent veil I have kept over everything.

'No,' I say to her, as soon as I can.

'No. Not well enough, at all. It was hard. Hard. It's getting harder all the time.'

SKIP

SKIP. Not just any kind of greyhound, but that half-dead wholly flatulent effort we use to keep under the stairs. Skip. He coiled up like a bad-tempered boa into the horse's collar in that dark recess that was more like a troll's lair, just off the scullery. In the gloom, all you could see was the stripped back gleaming chainsaw of his teeth if you came too near. Hear the nurr.... nurrrrr....nurrrr vibrations of his gulp-throated growl. Not what you could call a sociable animal.

What I remember most of all about him was his odour. Bad eggs, smelly wellies, decomposed rodent, manure heaps, mould, stale water, unwashedness, rancid skin conditions...it seemed to be a combination of all these and several more factors that made up his personal olfactory bouquet. I never knew a dog to smell so ripe. And his odour mattered, because my father revered him. There was no one in the canine world like Skip. He was the best rat-catcher in the country, or so my father said. I was willing enough to believe that about him. That dog was vicious enough to kill anything with a pulse, should they get on the wrong side of him. But his pong mattered most of all because my father used to take him into town every single day, in the back seat of the Triumph.

'Hey boy!' he'd shout into the troll's lair at eleven o' clock of a week day, 'are ya comin' to Bailieborough t'day, are ya?'

That was the cue for the greyhound to uncoil like a long lanky grey hose, magic himself out of his horse's collar, clatter out on his overgrown nails through a tide of Tibenzole containers, turf buckets and wellingtons onto the bare tiles of the scullery and finally shake loose his stale hard hairs onto the floor.

Then into the car with him, too self-important to wag his bent bucket handle of a tail at all of those he was leaving behind. Here was a dog who expected the world to be laid at his feet. A dog who took this as his natural lot. My father only encouraged his lordly behaviour by holding the back door open for him like a proper lackey and asking him to '*mind his tail*' when he got in, '*good lad.*'

The hound sat bolt upright in the back seat like Bodicea in her chariot whilst my father commandeered the whole navigational end of things from the steering wheel.

It was quite something to watch them go.

My father's seat had to be reclined as much as possible to accommodate his size and his arthritic leg, so his upper body was almost as far back as Skip's in the end up. The angle of his head was such that he was practically neck and neck with the greyhound and had a much better view of the interior of the car roof than of the road.

They were best left to make their 'on the road' trips by themselves, kind of like Bob Hope and Bing Crosby. However, one day it was my unfortunate luck to have to accompany them into town in order to get new school books from Brady's. The drive to Bailieborough was bad enough. My father really couldn't see much of what was happening outside the car. Add to that the fact that he had a policy of 'keeping well out from the ditch' which, on a narrow Cavan road meant that he ended up driving very much on the wrong side.

On top of that, his ability to brake or re-act quickly to any sudden encounters he might have was further marred by the bulky brown mittens he wore summer and winter for his bad circulation.

I sat in the back seat, in shotgun position to the hound because I hated the sight of him.

I suspended myself for as much of the journey as I could on
the palms of my hands until I thought my wrists were going to
snap. In the end, I gave in to utter bum collapse on the seat that
was littered with those despicable wiry dog hairs and the stench
that went with them.

We had just reached the hollow near Carngarve when, with
no warning whatsoever, the car's horn started blowing continu-
ously. My father puffed and panted and pressed his brown mitten down on it as if that would terrify it into silence. But no.
The horn was completely jammed and enjoying its blaring opportunity for a soliloquy.

On and on.

No stopping it.

Skip twitched his ears and his nose and with whatever cur
instinct he had for making a situation worse than it ever had to
be, let off a clanger. I rolled down the back window on my side,
and from outside, the sound of the horn came back at me.

Parrrrrrrrp! Arrrrrrrp! Parrrrrrrr! Parrrrrrrrrp!

On and on.

Right from the brae to the turn onto the main road, past
the doctor's house, St Anne's chapel. I was whitening with fear.
Surely it had to wear itself out? Everything else about the car
was crap; wouldn't the horn soon give up the ghost too?

But no.

On and on.

The hound still magisterially twitching his ears and looking
at life down his long nose as pedestrians to left and right on
Barracks St stared at us as we processed by.

My father in the front, red-jowled and getting redder, slamming his right mitten repeatedly on the steering wheel like a judge
with his gavel. Me in the back beside the noxious hound, wishing I could die several deaths so long as all of them rendered me
invisible.

It was with such a fanfare that I alighted from my chauffeur driven high-profile vehicle at Brady's in the middle of Main St. I was convinced that all the eyes of the town were upon me as I scorched my way into its sanctuary, for the first time seeing school books as a respite from something much worse. I still shudder at the sight of greyhounds.

March Upon Dublin

Doors bang.

Whistle blows.

Train slouches slowly out of Sligo station.

I settle back in my seat and pretend to read. What I'm really doing is watching the handsome man in the seat near the door pulling paperwork from an orange folder.

The pink froth morning is champagne uncorked. I can feel its celebratory bubbles under the thin skins of ice as we do the choo choo conga towards Collooney. Round black bales sit like giant plastic tablets in fields, cloistered in community together, white wafers of snow on top of each one to complete their habit.

I feel the land and the morning enter my soul. Like wire wool it coils into my being and for the remainder of the journey begins to weave a tapestry of thoughts, views and sentiment. Mentally, I am a magpie's nest of silver spoons and tinfoil, lost engagement rings and shiny paper. Everything stolen from everywhere else. I am gathering, just as the crows were starting to yesterday, last day of February.

Traditionally they build their nests today, the first of March every year. Big messy nests like bad perms, hanging deplorably from tall embarrassed trees.

I buy a coffee from the trolley as we are nearing Boyle.

It is boiled dishwater in a paper cup. There is a grey quality to its brownness. It is the kind of coffee that Frank Mc Court could write about and call poor, miserable, Irish Catholic coffee and get away with.

My situation is made better by knowing that the handsome man near the door with all the work in the orange folder is drinking the same coffee too.

We will suffer this one out together.

If we die, it will be a suicide pact.

We will hit the evening news as a tragedy.

I am glad I'm wearing my best trousers.

And matching underwear.

Little unoccupied homes of Connaught. Old three-roomed cottages, broken windows bolstered up with rusty barrels, sheets of galvanise or maybe even a full blown cataract of concrete blocks. Wintering cattle scratch their Friesian necks against what used to be orderly walls. Occasionally, in faded angry paint of history, the graffitied words of *Brits Out* on a gable end, acidic reminder of war in the seventies and eighties.

Darling homes of hopes and dreams, of potato drills and Yankee visitors; of night cheiles and tin whistle music, of children running shrieking and playing in the dizziness of summer with jammy bread in one hand, a water pistol in the other. 'I'll get you! I'll get you first!' through the crumbs.

Now nettles grow. Grass and weeds glue together what is left of the crumbling stone. Plumes of steam snort up from the Friesian faces as if they are snatching a quiet smoke behind the bicycle sheds of some crummy school. It's different, as all things get and most things are. There's a huge difference between crumbs, crumbling and crummy.

Mainstir na Buille...the Place of the Monastery. Boyle.

Much digging near the Boyle tracks as we pull in to the station. Dense sad clay is exposed, as dark as death and grieving. Scores of old sleepers have been awakened from the black blanket earth and piled urgently upon each other along the line, in preparation for active duty again. Wake up, wake up, take the strain, take the train, line up, lying down.

As we draw closer to Carrick I try to pick a long blonde hair out of my muffin and not be spotted doing it.

The handsome man with the orange folder is now gazing around him.

I hope I am suitably mysterious in my persona.

Choking over a hair-laden muffin would completely blow that image clean out of the water.

Crossing the Shannon is a mystical experience. Our most celebrated river divides the country, a liquid backbone between east and west, between being remembered and forgotten, privileged and not so. By Longford, the edges of the morning have softened. The pink sky has fizzed away like Alka Seltzer in a glass. It is now translated into a semi-transparent blue. Here and there, white afterthoughts of clouds are stroked thoughtfully across it, the morning rubbing its face awake with shaving foam on its fingers.

A station house top heavy as if on stilts is initially in silhouette.

It's like an anonymous person in a social documentary who says: '*I first started shooting strangers when I was four and a half...*'

Longford platform is empty.

All that occupies it are lights and shadows, solid red brick walls climb skywards. An unsat upon ivy-green bench holds up the fort. It's a Hopper painting waiting to happen.

The trees in the passing fields resemble a queue of hunchbacks waiting patiently in line for an osteopath. There's not a man-made stain on the landscape. The morning has been polished by God's breath. Icing sugar of winter shakes down through some divine sieve. The Irish words for frost and snow-*sioc agus sneachta* sound like thick crunchy biscuits crumbling on the tongue with just the right amount of swilled tea to melt them into paste, frost and snow, shook oggus schnock-ta, *sioc agus sneachta*.

Edgesworthstown, there's an old man with a too big cap on his head. Sports jacket tied with twine, green Wellingtons folded down to make a dirty white cuff just under the knee. He stands on the platform, his palm a shelf of fingers above his eyes. He stares in at every one of us staring out at him. His gaze is so intense that I feel convinced he will know us all for again, every man jack of us, will be able to pick us out of a gardai line-up. He doesn't waste a moment of our brief coming, being or passing but visually swallows us whole. There's a High Nelly Raleigh strewn against the box hedge. A batch loaf and a pint of milk peep coyly from a blue carrier bag on the handlebars. I can see already how he shall mount that old bicycle with sideways skill and cycle off, replete. Might spend his day with a radio, a spade and a collie. Will count some cattle, shake out some fodder, and say his prayers at the end of the night before pulling his white feet out of consciousness. I know he will salute us as we pull out of the station.

He does.

We pass through the bogs of the midlands. Dun colours of rush and peat with green conifer squares all sink down on their haunches. The bog is soft and spongy to the eye, dipping in the middle like an old feather bed. Sheep dot the surface, buttons and bobbles of white. Here the trees are soldiers. Waiting for the enemy. Thin and scrawny. Watchful. Crippled hedgerows catch the seams of each misshapen field, stitching between the patches of colour. Three lone cattle in a field. Hooves pointed, legs shapely, waiting for Riverdance music to set their limbs to bovine jigs and reels.

He puts the orange folder to rest. Takes his mobile from his waistband and dials a number, stares out the window, smiling while he waits to speak.

Ice is wrinkled cling film on a lake, keeping it fresh until the day peels it open.

Heat has crept in by Mullingar. The great stove of the earth is finally warming up; fire is now in the underbelly of life. A red plastic half-barrell in a field glows like a sacred heart lamp. The colour radiates much further than its small shape expects of it. Noble well-nourished oaks with stout hearts and strong arms stand in a circle near an ancient cemetery.

Another lake. It glistens to my right, immaculate and immense. Its shape opens out to infinity like a yogic breath. The trees beside it are bent to one side; they are men stooping their heads at the holy water font as they enter a chapel. The lake deserves that solemnity. Two swans elegantly sail pure white lives near the solitary island. My soul dips into the lake smooth as an oar.

He puts away the phone, still smiling.

It is good to know he loves someone.

I do not need to know who, why or how. This is a morning when love should simply be seen.

We will carry that flag as we March upon Dublin, February just one day behind us, the next nine months of this year yet to be taken.

MR BOND

I HAVE USED MOUSETRAPS, poison, positive thinking, negative thinking, three electronic doo-daws, blocked holes with brillo, wire wool and polyfilla but he's still with me. It's now gotten to the stage where I call him Mr Bond. The mouse, that is. Because it's a case of: 'Ah...Mr Bond, we've been expecting you.'

Yesterday I got up to find yet again no mouse in the mousetrap. More vexingly, there was no butter left in it either. Wretched thief. A friend gave me another 'pest-clear' electronic device yesterday. So I plugged that in last night, glad that this would be the last, ultimate, final straw for keeping out Mr Bond. Now I have four electromagnetic doo-daws blinking away all over the house and a lifetime subscription to the Nurofen Company.

He's as casual about it. Last night I came home at nine pm. A bright summer's evening. I met him mooching out from my sitting room into my kitchen. No wild rush or anything. Like this is his joint to wander around in and that is what he does. All he was missing was his smoking jacket and flamin' slippers.

'Excuse me, if there's anything I can help you with?' I say aloud to him, incredulous at his leisurely approach or seeming unawareness of me, the very mistress of this house. He looked at me in surprise as if I were a maid who'd gotten his room service wrong.

I now visualise myself coming home of an evening, entering my sitting room to find a lazy unkempt Mr Bond lying on his back on my coffee table with his hind legs up on my Paris coasters, the messy remains of a badly nibbled chocolate bar beside him. Twitching his whiskers, burping. And him saying to me: 'You're home late tonight, luv. Any chance you brought out some pizza? Man, I could just murder one o' them Cheese Supremes from the Bistro. Been thinkin' about it all day...' Excuse me, indeed.

This morning I woke up to find no butter in the mousetrap and a lot of mouse poo on the trap itself. And it hadn't even sprung. When am I going to finally get killing this little toe rag? Worse than that, I was making my tea at 7.45 when I smelt something like bad drains and I leaned down towards the washing machine to get a good old sniff. Suddenly, a little form skittered out from under the washing machine into my kitchen. Mr Bond. When he heard my shocked intake of breath he did a double take and retreated to the anonymous smelly safety of under the Hotpoint once more. Not before I roared at him: 'Mouse! We need to talk!'

Am I really meant to live with a mouse? I can't bear the thought. Even though Mr Bond does not seem to trespass onto table, counters or into gas oven, there is still no guarantee that he is not whiskering through my fruit bowl or snogging my parsnips and potatoes while I sleep. I am, to say the least, uneasy. Especially as I think I've been trying to fight this one pretty valiantly. What's it all about? So far, I've been accumulating a lot of mouse-opinions and advice from the general public:

Poison, it's the only way. No, they won't die inside; they'll go out to drink.

No, I wouldn't use poison, they'll die in your walls and cause an awful stink...they don't always manage to find their way back outside.

Poison? You mean bitch! Do you know what poison DOES? It swells up their stomachs so that their insides explode and they die in AGONY! You wouldn't use poison would you, you're not THAT mean???

Traps. Get a man to set them. Have you got a man?

They hate moth balls. Yeah, get yourself a load of mothballs and put them round the house.

The electromagnetic yokes are great, but you need to have them in a while to build up the beam.

Them electro-magnetic yokes aren't worth feck-all.

Buy airtight containers.

You have mice in SUMMER? God almighty, if you have mice in summer, what will you have in winter?

Feed him at the washing machine and he won't come any further. They like muesli or a wee bit of softened bread and butter. I used to feed mine nuts.

I played my didgeridoo against the wall whenever I heard him coming through. After three weeks he couldn't stick it any more and went away. I kinda missed him, you know.

Oghhh! You got a MOUSE in your KITCHEN? Not visiting YOUR house!

It's doing things to my mental health. In that I don't have much of it left. I am becoming more diabolical than Lucretia Borgia. For every mouse meal I lay down poison and cheese, poison and salad...or just plain poison. Come here, my pretty one, come here, my pretty!

Yes. I am Lucretia, against my will. I coldly sprinkle poison in Wedgewood saucers in my kitchen and behind my bookcase. Why has my four-legged enemy turned into Rasputin? I am forced to endure him, and I am going mad. I listen to every scratchy sound and get my camera ready on night-mode to click...somebody else must be a witness to this persecution, I cannot know it alone, go it alone...there is no one else here to see this infestation, but if I take pictures then maybe someone will believe me? Every jumping shadow is the mouse. Mr Bond has infested my brain, my hearing, my vision...I am cursed with busy floor patterns. Yet sometimes, it proves true. And I see him, looking at me from behind the farmer's chair, under the coffee table or from the top of the washing machine. Real and live and...indestructibly Bond. All I know is that I am not mad...yet. But I do not necessarily know whether or not I am on the way there. This cannot continue. For my sake or his. He is eating way too much cheese and poison. He will die of some high-cholesterol stomach disorder with excessive blood-thinning and inability to coagulate. It will take ages. I will end up tending him...as in the Three Blind Mice legend. He will have a gangrenous cut-off tail, diabetic blindness and dicky heart due to this terribly bad diet, be on disability allowance and I will be his resentful carer. This cannot continue. And no one will understand. That's the hardest bit. I can see my biographers delicately putting it that: '*Ms Lynch seemed to suffer excessively from nerves in latter years and her work strongly reflects this...mental unwellness. She dedicated the last five years to mouse-themed writings which make very little sense to the educated reader...*'

Oh, please let me still look young. Don't let the craziness ruin my skin. I will not be able to remain as sane as this for long...*hollow disturbing laughter*...no, I will not. Could you repeat that hollow laughter to fade please? Thank you.

SHARDS

I HAVE A HABIT. I don't know yet whether it is good or bad. I keep a sample of all the broken pieces of my life because I feel I can fix them. It will just take time, that's all. Thus far, I have a big wooden box of broken ceramics, chipped ornaments, even glass perfume bottles and I figure that one day - the perfect day - I can sit down and make the most wonderful mosaic mirror out of all this rubbish. Something that will reflect the most lustrous light containing these disembodied shards.

But right now, all I have is the box of rubbish and the belief that I can transform it.

Little over a year ago, my only brother took his own life. He was thirty six. I don't think I can accept this. This is a grief that burns acid into the heart.

No, I am far from acceptance. At best I have always been somewhat allergic to God and a grief such as this does not help matters.

Resurrection would be a dim dot on the horizon were it not for two significant things. Shortly after my brother's death, a friend from Georgia wrote to me in Ireland. She sent me a card with the signature of all twenty women in her Bible Study group. Each woman had written a small message of hope to me on the card.

The overall message was that they would pray for me every

day. This was the most amazing thing to me, that strangers would take my name, my family's name and my brother's tortured heart and drag it all to God, day after day in prayer.

I pictured these women, like spiritual ants, just keeping that prayer chain going. It was my way of realising that grief and mourning could be a communal thing. Across the Atlantic, that was a lifeline to me.

Much more recently, in the early days of January of this year, I was feeling a bit gloomy behind the counter of the shop where I work. Everything about the day was cobwebby, wet and dreary. I was rapidly going from gloomy to gloomier. January's grey days in the north-west of Ireland can do that for you. Sometime in the afternoon, a middle-aged lady came in and was buying something for her teenage son. I made an off-hand remark about teenage sons and it was then that the customer said that she didn't mind what purchase she had to make for her young lad, she would do it with love because just a year ago to that very day, her older boy had been killed in a car crash. I felt a shiver go through me as I recalled hearing about that dreadful road accident on the national news and wondering at the time what poor family was going though such heartbreak.

Now here was that boy's mother, standing in front of my counter, sad but with a dignity and beauty in the words she spoke about her son. From somewhere within her, a quiet faith knitted this dreadful tragedy into something that was a much bigger picture. It was as if she could see the spiritual equivalent of the mosaic that I am one day hoping to make. I felt a light enter me as she spoke. Unexpectedly I found myself telling her of my brother's tragic death. A hitherto unknown love went from me to her as we drew our conversation to a close. Though neither of us shed a tear during the encounter, I really felt that by the communal sharing of our mutual grief we had somehow both come away lighter. She asked my name and said she would pray for me and I asked hers (Teresa) and said I would pray for her.

I still do. Teresa's light has not left me. It is a positive strand of hope, rather than the dark grey of the cobwebs that often blanket me. A wonderful stranger like her becomes the very light source in my metaphorical mirror, reflecting hope and faith back to me by her presence and simple unself-pitying sharing. When Teresa walked into my shop that day, God was in her heart and through her he hijacked his way into mine.

In all sorts of shards and brokenness, there is the material for something truly beautiful; the much bigger picture as it were; whose meaning is interconnected with faith, hope and love and, because of all that, resurrection.

NUGGET

IT's FUNNY HOW Nugget shoe polish has stayed in my mind over the years. Its quaint 'dickey-bow' clip on the side was the beginning of the magic: pushing back that latch and then hearing the delicious tinny 'plop' as the tin sprang open, revealing the spicy pungent bouquet.

I was the shoe-shiner, ragging and buffing the Saturday evening pile-up for Sunday Mass. My father and brother both had size twelve feet, which led to shoes so big they'd nearly have to go to the crossroads to turn in them. I turned them out like black limousines, shining with the best of intentions for the Sabbath. I slid in my hand—almost the entire lower arm to the elbow—into each giant curragh of leather and first of all erased all signs of the week's comings and goings with a weather-beaten damp rag. After that came the rhythmic chant of fruity polish with the snub-bristled small brush. Then the bigger and much softer brush came with circular dance steps and long-limbed tango to bring out the sheen. But the most professional of the entire shoe-polishing team was also the most humble; an old woolen sock curled into a ball. It set the shine on fire so that you could see the blue glint of RTE news reporters telling their sightings from my father's leather toes during the News. As I polished, I could feel the strange empty impressions of my father bunions and my brother's long toes as each shoe told its side of the story.

I knew their feet inside out. The smell of Nugget shoe polish became as central to our Saturday nights as the fried bread supper, bath-time and ingesting every urbane witticism Gaybo uttered on *The Late Late Show*.

But Nugget also reminds me of Bridie, a cleaning lady in our neighbouring parish many years ago.

Bridie was the soul of clockwork responsibility who collected the keys of the chapel every Friday night from the teacher's house and spent the next two hours washing, waxing, scraping and shining that church.

However on this particular Friday night, she was only gone from the teacher's house fifteen minutes before they heard frenzied belting on their front door. Out goes Tommy, the man of the house, to discover Bridie on the doorstep and her face running blood from forehead to chin.

'In honour of God, Bridie,' he said to her as he pulled her in by the arm, 'What in hell happened ya?'

The poor woman was barely fit to stand and all she would come out with was:

'Jesus falls, Jesus falls.'

They sat her down by the fire and put a drop of whiskey in front of her but they still couldn't get an ounce of sense out of her. All she could say was,

'Jesus falls, Jesus falls, Jesus falls.'

Tommy decided there was nothing for it but to head up himself to the chapel and check out what class of mischief was going on there. He brought a big ash plant, a strong flash lamp and Caesar, the dog famous in the parish for having taken the sleeve out of the postman's jacket. And that's when the postman was in his van. There was no telling what part of the man would be missing if he hadn't the good fortune to be in the Renault.

The lights were still on in the church when they got that far. All Tommy saw in the main body of the chapel was Bridie's discarded bucket, wax and rags down near the back pews. Then he spotted what looked like a door knob lying in the aisle. He picked it up to discover it was the head of a Roman soldier. Further on a bit was some fella's plaster arm. All became clear to Tommy when he looked up at the wall. One of the Stations of the Cross had fallen and must've hit poor Bridie on its way to the floor.

The name of the station that had collapsed was *Jesus falls the First Time.*

He spent the next ten minutes gathering soldiers' arms, swords and legs. It was Caesar who managed to paw out the head of Jesus from under the confessional. When Tommy landed back to the house with all the station pieces gathered up in his coat, Bridie nodded and said again:

'Jesus falls.'

'Thought, then,' said Tommy to her, 'you'd want to be horrid feckin' careful when he goes to fall the second time.'

He spent that night and most of Saturday gluing the pieces back in place with *Uhu* and *Evo Stick.* The kitchen was high with the smell of glue and gloss paint, where he had touched up the chipped sides of the frame.

The biggest problem was all the unsightly white scars on the faces of Jesus and the Roman soldiers.

The teak gloss wouldn't be right for those scars. The answer presented itself when he saw his wife shining the shoes for Sunday. So…with a wee rag moulded around the tip of one forefinger he applied a glowing sheen of black Nugget shoe polish to the jagged plaster faces.

And to this day, there's still one Cavan parish where Jesus unintentionally gets to be a black man with a fruity complexion.

CLOSE TO NORMAL

CONCERN CHRISTMAS FAST. 27th November 2004. This is what normal people were doing: shaking tins and briefly going hungry for good causes. Not what I was doing. Going up to a garda station to have a friendly chat. Then in the barracks, answering questions and smiling at the mug I was drinking from. It had a pig design. The Cavan guards have a sense of humour, fair play to them. I know I said that much. A friendly pig on a cheap mug. It's strange, but that's one of the things that held me together.

I remember the day so well. A November day that shone like June. A Saturday, a morning of frost and promise. We drove eastwards through Glencar valley, I the passenger, my friend the driver. It was so unbelievably beautiful. It is hard, sometimes, to see Ireland looking so eerily gorgeous at the wrong time of year. The light that came from the sun, bathing Kings Mountain, was pink. Champagne, celebratory pink. We were going to Cavan for my elderly aunt's funeral. Bridgie's death was not a cause for sorrow. I felt grateful for her life and that she was being laid to rest on such a beautiful day. Hers had been a kind life, well-lived but so full of pain and endurance it was good to know that she had been cut free.

What seemed strange in a rural Cavan parish was the sight of a couple of uniformed guards loitering outside the chapel as her coffin came out. Then, as we followed the hearse to the graveyard, the strangest thing happened. We saw another hearse coming out from a side road. How funny, we thought— because that's the way our sense of humour goes, this could be a Keystone Cops adventure, what if we stupidly end up following the wrong hearse. Yeah. It made us smile, the very idea.

In the graveyard, while my aunt is being buried, there are still guards watching. It is only in the hotel half an hour later that one of them approaches me and asks me to come upstairs to a private room. That's where he tells me, with regret, what he has to tell me. I now dully realise that the other hearse we had seen contained the body of my brother as he was being brought down to the morgue in Cavan for the post mortem.

I must leave the place. All I know is that I can't stay in Cavan that night. I must get home, Sligo is home and it is important that there is some normality or I will leave my mind. My friend drives me, the same route that we took earlier that morning. But now we have another funeral on our mind and it will be in the same chapel.

I have no idea how I will get through the next few days, or how long they will be. My brain is packed with dead matter. My face is heavy as cast concrete. I have no idea if this is even real. An uncle's words are playing around in my head 'this has never happened in our family before.'

No. It is not a thing to be prepared for.

My friend drives me, in mostly silence. I cannot bear music and I cannot bear talk. I cannot cry or be anything. I look out the black view, know we are going through Glencar again, but this time there is nothing to be seen and I wonder how it could have been so unearthly dazzling this morning, so perfect that I was airlifted by its beauty, had even been happy going to a funeral.

I tell my friend that I don't want to go home. I want to go to the supermarket. I need milk. There is no milk for tea in the house.

We drive to Tescos. We go in. Under all that bright phoney

light, I walk the aisles, dry-eyed, unbelieving, staring at every product with the fascination of an alien, but not knowing really what I came in for. I just didn't want to be still, didn't want to reach wherever it was I was going, hit the wall that would stop me from all these sideways distractions. The wall that would jar me with the reality of what the guards had told me. The realisation that would hit me—sooner or later—that it was actually all true. That my brother had ended his own life at 36 and that somehow this was all part of mine. No. I could not take that in just yet.

I watched other shoppers debating which firelighters to buy, how many bottles of sparkling water, clunking tins of Kit-e-Kat and Pedigree Chum into their trolleys, wheels eeking, perfume wafting. I brushed by them, like a ghost myself. Would any of them believe me if I told them how my day had been spent? Excuse me; my brother took his life this morning. I think I'm in bad shape but I don't know yet. I imagine saying that. No, it's not real. That's not the kind of thing you say. And this isn't the way it happens, all this civilisedness. No bloody way. I don't think I feel anything but I'm afraid of when I will. This is all going to hurt. I wonder how many people wander round super-markets with huge news in their heads that they want to tap strangers on the shoulder with. Life has stopped being normal for me and I don't want to believe that other people are living normal lives while I am living this. That's what I think as I pass the frozen foods and the chilled section and the special two-for-one offers on the six pack yoghurts and easi-spreads.

We go home without the milk because it didn't make any difference. That's what I told my friend. I just wanted to be somewhere with the lights out, with sheer nothingness. I didn't know what was ahead or how long it would last, but for now, I just wanted numbness and nothing. Nothing, nothing. Nothing was the very best I could hope for.

Doing Nothing With Bluebirds

HERE IT IS SO EASY to get nothing done.

'Here' is Nada monastery, Crestone, Colorado.

Here's what I'm doing with my time.

I'm sitting outside, sipping coffee in the Adirondack chair. Watching a hopping bird with a red skull cap moving across the sandy terrain towards me. It's like he's on a pogo stick. He's a stranger in these here parts. A quick spot of research pins him down as being a Towhee.

The bird feeder isn't wobbling at all this morning. It's calm.

A gentle breeze blows my hair dry. 9.35 a.m. Colorado sky is muted bluey grey white like a Constable painting.

A plane rumbles somewhere in the sky's vast stomach.

My regular neighbour, Mr. Bluebird, perches on the log pile. Mrs. Bluebird is probably hard at work in the nest under the eaves:

Cleaning and sweeping hearth and floor
And fixing on their shelves again
Her white and blue and speckled store.

Oh now, there she is.

She has suddenly appeared on the bird feeder. She's such a dainty little thing, and more brown than blue, like she's wearing a smock for her housework.

She makes the feeder wobble on its upright. It could be because she's craning her neck to get a good look at what I'm up to. She's never quite made up her mind about me. I hope that she realises that I've been her water sponsor for the last six weeks and if it wasn't for me, that birdbath would've been miserably empty outside my window.

To advance our relationship, I start talking over to her, telling her how gorgeous she looks today. She leans her head to one side as if shyly taking on the veracity of this statement. I am sure Mr. Bluebird does not shower her with compliments much nowadays, although I have seen him flying home from work with the occasional insect takeaway, fair play to him.

I enquire cautiously after her family.

Are all her young ones raised and on their way to independence?
Little Boy Bluebird, how's he doing?

I must confess, I was a bit worried recently about Little Boy Bluebird. He was flying right into the hermitage window on a continuous basis and I thought he'd never pull through the training phase. I was fearing a bit about brain damage. I voice this concern to her and she twists her head around with a jerk as if to imply that it wasn't her side he took after.

Does she have plans for more family, I ask?

I imply that it can't be that easy for her to be a homemaker with Mr. Bluebird being the gadabout that he is, forever slacking off on the woodpile. Flitting to every pinyon in the land to rest his weary butt while she maintains the nest. She leans her head to the other side and I believe the truth of this matter has hit home to her and she's glad somebody understands. Even a foreigner who speaks funny.

To further strengthen the blossoming friendship between us and to show her that I am somewhat like a bird myself in the talents I possess, I start to hum an Adiemus track. She's fascinated. Transfixed. The head now going like crazy.

She's wildly impressed, I can tell. I build on this by launching into *Come Back Paddy Reilly To Ballyjamesduff,* just to share a little bit of my Irish culture with her but I've hardly gotten to the '*bridge of Finea*' bit before she's flown off in aural disgust.

What have I done wrong?

Or sung wrong?

Oh well. Can't win 'em all.

Maybe I would've fared better if I'd started with '*There'll be bluebirds over the White Cliffs of Dover.*'

I'll try that tomorrow.

ANNIVERSARY

WELL, I cried and I cried and I cried.

Came undone up in the chapel. Around consecration time, I think.

The geysers of salt water decided to explode mirthlessly from the Lynchian mount Rushmore façade. And on and on and on they went, into every crevice of skin I have. I mean, into my ear drums and down my neck kind of tears. Back and front of neck, kind of tears.

Hot boiling ones, the size of hailstones.

I'm now rotted right through.

How stupid am I? Going to Mass with no such thing as a decent tissue?

I had one yellow serviette from who knows what occasion in the pocket of the cardigan borrowed from Liz. God knows, it could've been hers. She could've been using it as an emergency device to unplug her children's noses or wipe bird poo off their Sunday hair. I used it anyway.

I also had a white woefully disintegrated tissue in my jeans pocket. I used both, to the point of saturation. By the time communion came, I wasn't sure if I resembled some kind of humanoid walrus with possibly yellow tissue-based tusks leaping out from my nostrils.

And after communion, more and more tears, less and less tissue.

It's my brother's second anniversary tomorrow, you see.

And I can't keep this kind of thing in. It's emotional sludge, consisting of freefall debris of grief and guilt and loss and all things unknowable wrapped in sorrow and given tears as a body. This is the only real way I know it's all still in there, all this hurt and shock.

Against me and against him. For me and for him.

All this. And not one decent tissue to soak it up.

And I wonder what kind of Divine Joke God is, that he lets this happen, all of this.

And watches, from wafers and wine.

Last year, this same thing happened to me on the Sunday near Eddie's first anniversary. The same nature of grief explosion. Nothing could stop those tears. There I was near the front of the chapel. I left as soon as I could after Mass. I was feeling really fragmented, and so, so alone.

Grief does not cause you to believe you are surrounded by a gang load of your nearest and dearest. No, it singles you out like a lone antelope and chases you across unsheltered plains.

And that is why last year, when I left the chapel, I didn't realise I was speeding.

All I was aware of was that I needed to get somewhere and that my face was oozing tears.

Then I saw the flashing light behind me, the siren. Unmarked garda jeep.

My hands were shaking on the wheel as I pulled over.

I undid my seatbelt and reached into the glove box to see if I had my licence there.

A looming garda is now outside my driver's window. I don't even see his face. Just big hands. It's like a bizarre alternative confessional. Anonymous. Impersonal.

'Licence please,' his voice says. I give it out to him, I see my hand is still shaking.

Oh God, this will look like I'm a fucking drunk.

'Do you know what speed you were doing back there?' he asks me.

I think for a moment.

'Was it over sixty miles an hour?' I quaver.

I really hadn't a clue in all the world what speed I had been doing.

'It's kilometres we go by in this country,' he said crisply. 'You were doing a hundred and thirty in a hundred kilometre zone.'

Sweet Jesus. I'm really sorry to hear that.

I say back to him, 'look, I know it's no defence, but my brother took his own life this time last year and I really need to get to a friend's house. It's a bad day.'

First there's a silence.

I'm aware of seeing his face for the first time.

Or the lower part of it.

The official mouth, middle-aged looking. He has lowered himself.

How long is this silence?

He says then—awkwardly—'Here, put that belt on you, if another guard stopped you he'd pull you for that.'

'But I only took it off to get my licence for you!' I wailed at him, thinking somewhere in my normally very irrational mind that this was very unfair in a rational world. And I feel the new tears starting to stream down my face again replacing the old ones. He'll have me up for lack of driving visibility next.

'I know you did, I know you did,' he said.

He reached his hand in to pull my seat belt down a bit from its holster and put the latch of it into my right hand.

'Put it on you there now, like a good girl,' and as I took it from him he patted my still shaking hand and said more kindly:

'You'll be alright now, so you will, you'll be alright. Take care now and slow down a little bit. You'll be alright. Take your time now till you're ready. You'll be alright.'

He backed off out of my sight to the flashing blue light behind me.

I sat in my stilled car, seat belt on, tears streaming but I felt comforted. I felt heard. And when I did start up that engine and drove the rest of the way to my friend's place, there were no more tears. They had literally been stopped by the God squad. As I drove, I recalled that the last time I'd been talking to a garda was when one had taken me aside after Aunt Bridgie's funeral to tell me that Eddie had taken his life that morning. How bizarre. How awfully bizarre.

That was Eddie's first anniversary.

This is his second. I will get through this one too and maybe, like last year, the help will come from an unexpected source.

Miss You

Does a fly live deliberately to annoy humans?

There is a bluebottle right now circling like the feckin Red Baron round my head.

It's January. Ireland. Shouldn't I be spared this kind of torture?

He lands on the lip of my mug.

He sees my hand coming.

Off.

Then onto the lip of my glass.

All the time his circulating buzz. The circular saw of his circulating buzz. The circles he saws as he buzzes. The circling sound as he saws.

Go away, I say.

For God's sake, Go away!

I sound stupid. Telling a big-assed bluebottle to go away.

Like he's going to.

Like he cares what I ask him.

Like he understands.

Like I have saintly authority to transcend all sorts of boundaries between incompatible species and made him biddable —either through him solicitously leaving the hermitage with a gentle chiff of the door or else sitting like a talisman of quiet inspiration on my shoulder.

I totally AM stupid. I say the go away thing again and cringe. I sound like a het-up heroine in a Jane Austin novel. Ineffectual. Between love dilemmas, waiting for the vicar and his wife to come calling for tea and cucumber sandwiches and my goodness, this wretched affair, whatever shall be done. If I were a Raymond Carver anti-hero I'd take off my shoe and shoot the fly. In staccato descriptions. Or take out a penknife and shoot it. Or walk into my neighbour's apartment say nothing for the entire story, pick up a New York Times and shoot it. To take up a gun and shoot it would be much too crass.

It is silence here.

He is an enemy when he's quiet because I know he has the power to make noise whenever he wants to. And he will. And when he wants to will not be when I want to. Because, let's face it, I never want to hear the buzzing buzzard again.

Totally quiet. Like he's all buzzed out. He's not the biz with no buzz. He's lost his fizz, my busy buzzless bluebottle.

Now.

I don't believe this.

I feel concern for him.

Where are you, my little poppet? Where art thou, my winged wretch? Where can you hide in silence?

What has made you lose your annoying tongue?

What battle of wills is it that I have won?

I feel alone now. The aloneness of having lost a life companion whose habits have always annoyed me. The sloppy wet towels on the bathroom floor. The chewed up biros at the phone. The milk supply depleted in the fridge, smeary jam stains in the butter, my chocolate hoard looted, mugs of half drunk cold tea with livery skins abandoned throughout my living space like domestic refugees. All these irritating companionable things. That I'd rather endure than live with the absence of the companion.

Bluebottle, I miss you.

Finding God In A Vacuum

I WAS GIVEN a regulation blue stand-up kind of hoover for this task and all in all it should have been a low key domestic event. My mission: To vacuum the little chapel in the monastery.

The first problem was a simple one. A tube thing fell on the floor like a snake, unleashed from its regular hang-out on planet hoover. This thing then bobbed and weaved itself in front of me like a giant plastic worm. It was topped by one of those attachments for objects that people never vacuum, like pleats of curtains, pelmets and behind the cushions of sofas. The fun and games started when I attempted to put it back into its circular holster somewhere on the hoover. There were many places on the hoover where it looked like it might fit - but didn't. In the end I wedged it into some round notch that held the giant plastic worm's neck in place but still allowed its large serpentine body to whirl around at excited moments and belt me on my right leg.

I started vacuuming. The weight of the thing!

On top of that, it took a lot of shunting to and fro, to and fro, to and fro before the hoover thought itself equal to the task of picking up a fallen geranium leaf under the chapel window. No sooner had it picked up the leaf than it suffered an allergy to the whole notion of geranium ingestion and spat the damn thing out under the Tabernacle. To and fro, to and fro, to and fro. Lifted the geranium leaf once more. Then spit. Lift and spit. Lift and spit. It became a pattern. And I, to show you the headstrong being that I am, stuck with the idea that the hoover was the one who should stoop to picking up the geranium leaf. To and fro, to and fro. Lift and spit, lift and spit. To and fro, lift and spit....I am building up the speed of anger as I shunt my Panzer tank over that leaf for the umpteenth time. But to no avail. Eventually I pick it up with my own bare hand.

This act of heroism on my part obviously causes the hoover to regroup with its inner antichrists. It decides to throw another dilemma at me.

I'm up under the altar at this stage - a relatively clean piece of carpet. To and fro, to and fro and I'm about to go elsewhere when I see a trail of grit on the area I've just worked. I shunt my Panzer at it. While it lifts no grit on the 'to' movement it seems to disgorge more of it on the 'fro'.

I take a closer look at what is happening.

The hoover is picking up nothing yet due to some unspeakable intestinal trouble, it's spitting out stuff from its rear end as it shuntles along. Stuff like dog hairs, paper clips and debris not usually associated with the chapel carpet. And yes, there's my old friend again, the geranium leaf.

I lie the machine down flat in the recovery position and poke down its throat with my index finger. Can't find any wedge of balled up dirt which might be causing this latest health crisis. No opportunity for Hoover Heinlich manoeuvre. I stand up to switch on the appliance from hell again and clock my skull off the Tabernacle above me. My head is impaled by shards of God-sent pain.

I drag the hoover over to a *Prie Dieu* and use this location as my electric domestic appliance pit stop and start it up. It belches a cloud of grey dust out its tail end. I turn off the machine and examine all those misleading orifices again. This square thing here...the filter. Clean. Ish. Move on. This thing here. Another filter...thing. Once again, startlingly clean, given that it lives in a hoover. A door...thing...falls off and reveals the hoover bag, but not before it attempts to knife me on the shin. I feel the bags' pudgy body. Nearly empty. I clamp that door back on and once more examine the hoover in prone position. Well, the hoover is in prone position, I'm on hands and knees, confusingly looking like a devout Muslim duly facing Mecca. I stare down its throat again and feel a small bunch of stuff, barely within reach of my fingertip. I poke and prod with that struggling fingertip, dragging what I can of my findings literally by a hair until I get a better grip. Out comes a wad of balled up dust. I reach in again. Another agonised pulling session resulting in the birth of a second blob of dust ball. And again. And again. Dust quadruplets. I feel very very proud of myself as I stand the machine back upright.

I lift the hoover tenderly by its neck out from behind the Prie Dieu pit stop and...its head falls off.

I am left holding what looks like an AK47 while the floor-bound part of the hoover remains...floor-bound. I bend down and try to match orifice to sticking-out bits. At any rate, jamming action marries brute force. The parts seem to fit back together.

I am a great girl, I tell myself. Yes, truly, one of the best.

I lift my prized domestic appliance out once more from Pit Stop Area One.

The head falls off.

I'm beginning to strongly resent the four balls of new-laid dust that are sitting in front of me like grey fluffy eggs. The plastic worm comes alive at this point, swings around, claps me on the leg and then falls out of its holster. It uncurls its narrowed head as it arrows towards the floor and with a vehement thud disperses two of my dust balls into a levelled out plane of ...dust and grit and dog hair. And a paper clip.

I lift the hoover and...the head falls off.

Jesus, Jesus, Jesus, where are you in this???!

Brute force, jamming, orifices, sticky-out bits, temper, temper, temper.

The head stays on.

I switch on the hoover and await progress. It comes quickly. The hoover wants to chew up the entire mat in front of the altar. *Wheeee-oooo-eeeee-ooooo-eeeee-ooooo-eeeeee!* it whines as it grasps a corner of the previously tranquil mat in its jaws and now attempts to swallow it whole in the manner of, say, a boa constrictor and a rabbit. It finally relinquishes the mat and finding its own cable, attempts a little act of self-cannibalism. I smell a faint burning as the hoover hots up its efforts to digest more of its delicious lead. There're dust clouds forming around and about, wafting under the tabernacle in the manner of profane incense and the floor is still crunchy with grit.

I have had enough.

I find the 'off' button and press it firmly.

It's three days of darkness and dust balls.

It's from dust we came and to dust we shall return.

It's '*where you saw only one set of footprints that's where I carried you, my child, through acres of gritty carpet with paper clips and dog hairs and the occasional missing earring.*'

It's not much in the line of comfort.

It's also Jesus saying, '*now* see what I came to save, and the seeming impossibility of it. And yet, so, so worth it. You're all so, so worth it, you little aggravating loveable pile of dust-balls, non-functioning hoovers...both. I love each tiny particle that you consist of. Each mysterious grain that forms you. And I know you better than anyone. Better than any dust doctor. Better than any hoover manufacturer. I can fix every seemingly unfixable part of you. I know every inch of you and every microcosm of every inch of you and where and what in this world you fit into and how and why. And every inch of you and every microcosm of every inch of you is perfect for that which you are meant to be and do. You flawed, exasperating, clueless beings, you are meant to last forever. You're that good, that worth it, that so utterly worth it. You were designed by the top man in the business. A God among men, a man among gods. Both. You are quality. You carry my name as your brand. You just don't follow your own manufacturer's instructions. But if you did, oh boy!'

Pick up your cross and follow me.

Sometimes a cross is shaped just like an awkward hoover. And sometimes we are.

All the same, I decide I'll switch my blue hoover for the red one.

So I pick up the hoover.

The head falls off.

Starbucks. Coffee Shots
And Snapshots

Starbucks, the Plaza, Santa Fe. Sunday 6th July. 2006. The most American-of-American guys sits to my immediate right.

Salmon t-shirt with college insignia, Teva flip-flops, cream cargo shorts with subtle label too small and over-priced to interpret, baseball cap with hieroglyphic team logo too American for me to de-cipher.

He flicks through a new camera manual and from time to time picks up a heavy Canon. The brand is almost too discreet to make out but I've been staring - in my own surreptitious Irish tourist kinda way - for the last ten minutes.

So, from time to time he picks up his heavy Canon with eighteen foot zoom lens and a cockpits worth of buttons and twistables. He plays with it solemnly, interchangeable looks of bemusement and wonder crossing his face before he puts it down again and takes up the manual. He seems to find the manual heavier than the camera.

He's got tanned hands and remarkably clean finger nails.

The man at the table just in front of me is not so typical. He is black. Though that is not why he's not so typical. He is possibly in his late thirties though - at the risk of sounding racist - I find it hard to tell with black people. He wears a black shirt and cream chinos. In front of him is a music score. Beside that is a very thin, very, very discreet mobile phone.

In his right hand is a—and I have to look twice to confirm this—tuning fork. From time to time—I like this about him —he hums aloud.

A high tinny hum like maybe what Lenny Henry would do before he goes into something really funny. Then sometimes he conducts the music while his lower lip bubbles and puckers with low noises. His eyebrows drive their way up and down his forehead like wipers on a Land Rover.

He looks out the window frequently, eager for distractions, it seems. Like me, he welcomes the passing fare of Sunday amblers with their American-sized dogs. The pretty girls, the fit guys, the blobby, wobbly tourists in Hawaiian shirts with their de-cerebralised expressions that speak of Gary Larson characters from head to toe.

Now he puts on a broad-brimmed black hat—is it a fedora— with a snakeskin-coloured hat band.

He hauls what could be a music case or laptop from the floor.

Tuning fork pocketed and sheaf of music under left arm he walks out of my life, through the double doors and to the right.

I am left with a sensation of indefinable satisfaction. It's like the feeling which accompanies that vital delicious hush—existing for just a second or two—after a brilliant performance and before the rapturous applause.

NATIVITY SCENE

IT WAS EVIDENT EARLY ON that Mary was destined to become a single mother. Possibly due to the insensitive handling of messages by a five year old Angel Gabriel.

Gabriel, it has to be said, had his own problems what with his clothes hanger tinsel-entwined wings coming askew under his oxter. But all the same, the vicious manner in which he jabbed his wand in the face of Mary's betrothed and told him in barking oration that: '*This wumming would have a son a gawd and name him Jeeeeesuss*' was enough to unhinge any adult male, let alone a four year old Joseph with table linen for robes.

Joseph went into a major hissy fit, tore the towel off his head and burst free of the restraining grip that his mother had actually managed to keep on him up to now. With the instinct of any good mum, she had ridden into this situation expecting some kind of hitch along the way. Thus she had tethered the Joseph and Mary combo firmly in front of her, using thumb and index finger of each hand to langle them together like goats.

Too much for Joseph. Too soon. And being made to stand near a girl who wasn't even his own sister? This was, for him, the start of a very bad Christmas. He was fully within his four year old rights to kick his mother in the shins and run screeching down the aisle straight into the 'I-told-you-so' smug arms of his father.

Joseph's mother is left grasping the empty air with her right hand, hopping on one leg whilst still maintaining a grip on the abandoned Mother of God. The Reverend, though having just lost almost half his cast, is still gung ho bent on delivering the rest of the Nativity Scene to his flock. This entails encouraging Mary to drag the grey stuffed pillow case cast as the donkey hither and thither under the pulpit while all in church belt out *Silent Night*.

The angel Gabriel, not one for slacking on his side of things, feels that Mary could make that donkey trot a little faster, so he lashes out with his wand a couple of times as she passes him on her apathetic way to Bethlehem. Mary bursts into some pre-natal depression of such intensity that the night can no longer be in any way perceived as silent.

Joseph's mother, keeping a close grip on the back of Mary's roaring neck, beckons to a woman in the congregation. This woman is Mary's real life mother, who reluctantly comes forward to haul her hysterical daughter and stuffed pillow case donkey down to the body of the church. Joseph's mother returns to the pew where Joseph is still getting post-traumatic counselling from his father. The father now throwing her a look that hangs onto its 'I told-you-this-was–never-going-to-work-out' smugness of before. She sits in, tight-lipped, beside him, arms folded.

Trotting her twin props of My Little Pony and Barbie re-peatedly across the pew, she's oblivious to the Christmas col-lapse happening all around her. She's possibly four years old and dressed adorably in a 101 Dalmatians fur coat. Her golden hair is spun like sunshine and reflects the light of the Church candles guttering in the holly-wreathed windows. It is peace and joy itself to look at her. There she is, humming away to herself, her own little song. She runs into difficulty trying to dress My Little Pony in a sequinned bolero that she has just wrestled off Barbie. My Little Pony doesn't have the physique to carry it off or indeed even take it on. I see a frown furrow-ing her pretty brow. Then she grasps both pony and doll in each hand and starts battering them to plastic death on the edge of her pew.

We sing out the night on Adeste Fideles, speeding it up a bit as we recall the promise of mulled wine and mince pies in the hall afterwards. Now that the Reverend himself has put a Tiny Tears Jesus into the manger, there's not a lot else to hang around for. This is the best Christmas Carol Service I have ever been at. So full of real honest to goodness life.

LIFE THROUGH THE LONG WINDOW

THERE WERE THREE PERSONALITIES reflected through those windows.

One faced the road - that was the sociable one - from which I anticipated the visitors and dwindling returns of the Triumph, Mazda or whatever decrepit old car we happened to have at the time. You could see all the way over the hills to Bailieborough.

'Look,' my father would say, 'Loughanlea is horrid close-lookin' today, that's not a great sign of the weather.' The sill held used Ely cartridges and loose change in a glass bowl. The red geranium. A pair of rosary beads balled up like goats droppings in a corner. And a Jews harp, seldom played.

The middle window looked out over a rolling vista of neighbours fields. But first it had to give the clothesline centre stage. The billowing sheets, the marionettes of long johns doing jigs and reels with long-sleeved white vests, the good shirts, the old shirts, the work clothes stiff with paint and dung no matter how thoroughly washed they were. The frosted clothes in the winter. Breaking them off the line like brittle twigs in the evening, crushing their crunch into a curve over my arm as I fetched them in like corpsed war casualties from the red-nosed dusk.

The last window, the yard one, facing back towards the gable end of the hen house, the hayshed and the granary steps. The arrivals and departures of visitors heralded by Buff the Labrador who was chained to the outer granary wall. The departure of balers and harvesters, blessed and sprinkled by my mother with holy water as they passed from the yard down the lane to carry out their seasonal chores with prima donna cooperation. Buff barked them off like an enthusiastic cheerleader while hens scarpered to left and right with hysterical clucks and panic-driven strides to hiding places under trailers.

But that's not even it. That's not even in the heart of it. It was where those windows looked out from that was important.

That kitchen was the epicentre, the nerve centre, the community centre of our home. It was never luxurious and now I look through family photos and see the mad colour schemes on the wall—two tones in the seventies. A dark gloss red on the bottom half that wouldn't show the dirt and that would take a rub of a cloth easily. A jaunty custardy yellow manned the upper half of the wall. A trimmed cove of blue at the top pulled the whole endeavour together before we struck into the mustard ceiling. My God. It all looked so poor...Were we poor? Though if we were wasn't everybody? We were a hardworking family, that's all I know. Just like any farming family. There were no luxuries like holidays, my father never got away from the farm for a day in his whole life since he got married. Breaks were taken for funerals, weddings and maybe one afternoon a year at Bettystown. That kitchen was as cyclical as our year. The middle window and the letter rack conveyed the passing of time, the Christmas cards, the St Patricks Day cards, the summer wedding invitations, the Autumn Back to School lists, tick tock, tick tock.

Tick tock, tick tock now.

I go all sorts of roundabout ways to avoid driving by my old home. That front window frowns down on the road, a long steel window, a long lingering look. That's what I no longer want to see.

I have avoided writing this. Or anything that could possibly take the shape of this. A book. Between two covers. It cuts too deep, that raw razor blade cut that looks so clean. You stare at the marginal line incised on the skin. Why, it doesn't look like a cut at all. And you nearly can't believe it's there until the pearls of blood pop out and then the oozing and the pain...and the fear of how deep it all is. How unstoppable.

Who doesn't have the huge gasping moments in their lives when they feel their spirit cannot take any more, that this is now the ultimate in what can break a human heart? My home place has that sort of agonised quality. I wish there was someone there whom I could visit, just one shoulder to gently shake to ask what happened here, where does anybody think this might have started going wrong? I can't believe my brother's death, the awful jaw-dropping tragedy, the unresolved guilt and mish mash of feelings that comes from knowing that someone whom I grew up with, shared Weetabix with, played Lego with, fought over ice cream portions with, would take their own life. I can't look at photographs of anything to do with my home now without some kind of Chernobyl smoke arising from all that should be formative and comforting. I look through the three windows and I see nothing.

I was fifteen when I thought I would kill myself. I had good reason. My exams were due to start soon. I decided I would take an overdose of Anadin, just like a girl I'd read about in a story. I ran into complications when I searched high up and low down for Anadin in the house. I could only find four disprins and disprins are much too domestic with which to end your life when you're fifteen. Oh there were plenty of things like Calamine lotion, lice shampoo and Algipan and weird things named Anusol which gave very unpleasant directions about external use and bowel motions. But no Anadin. I'd have to wait until the weekend and buy my own when I got my pocket money. It was going to be such a waste. Of pocket money. When Friday finally came, I stood staring out my bedroom window, mesmerised as always by the water tank below, looking for the eel that lived there, whipping and curling his long form round and round and round that squat oblong tank. I thought all manner of things to myself. I didn't want to spend my last money on this earth on stupid Anadin. My parents should be organised enough to have it in the house. Good parents would. They'd have plenty of it. Besides, the situation was slightly more hopeful in that I had done a bit of revision and maybe I'd scrape through maths with a grade D. There were other people in my class who were worse. And there were some who were plain stupid. Not that that would be any consolation to my father, who would be only interested in the honours and whether I would do better than so and so down the road. Besides, I couldn't possibly kill myself this weekend, because it was the annual Killabeg Carnival from Friday till Monday. I couldn't possibly mess up the only week-end that my mother and father ever got out of the house. They especially enjoyed the Friday night, meeting all sorts of neigh-bours and old friends down in the beer marquee and discussing who was going to Big Tom or Joe Dolan. I mean, it would ruin it altogether if they had the body of their only daughter lying dead in the house for them to deal with when they came home. And if my funeral were to be on the Sunday, that means they would miss the bonny baby competition and the sheep dog trials and my father would surely kill me over that. At the very least, there would be bad feeling. Not to mention the divided loyalties for the neighbours in terms of who in their family would represent the rest of them at my funeral and whether all the others would still pack themselves into a convoy of Toyotas and Datsuns, clean up their babies faces and head off down to Killabeg for the craic. It was much too complicated. Much, much. I decided to hang onto life until the Intercert results were due to come out. There would be plenty of time to kill myself then, and hope-fully by that stage I would've saved up over the summer months for Anadin or my mother would've cottoned onto herself and bought some in for the house.

Pain can sometimes be crutched by humour. I have to do

that. I have to do it, to stop myself from that pointless torture of looking for reasons. Life is so much wider than one person, one reason, one answer. And even though I look back on that silent but temporary misery of the fifteen year old me, I wonder how much of my own brother's unhappiness was equally silent, unshared. And in how many homes right across Ireland...and further...are there strangers in families living together whilst not wanting to live at all.

Here I am, in my head, trying to polish the glass, trying to see into what can never truly be seen. Tip toe standing, looking for light in that three-windowed kitchen.

These October Days

I AM INTRIGUED by the lengthiness of these October days. The stinging freshness as I look out the kitchen window down through the sing song rattle of those sycamore leaves.

On my horizon is a whole vast ocean to glitter for me by day.

By night it's the wink and visual twitter of Strandhill street lights—a faraway necklace of illumination against the pitch black throat of darkness.

I am cloistered in quiet, stillness the gown that cloaks me. When I touch the night with my fingers it breathes its realness against me like the warm grassy snorting of a cow. Even in such utter peace I know I am drowning in the real.

An owl takes rest during the day within those fluttering sycamore leaves. More and more the clawing of its upright branches and twigs become exposed. One day it will awake completely naked and grab at the sky forlornly like a grieving widow, looking for the sun to warm its wooden bones. Crying for spring to bring in its wardrobe change.

Two days ago I was at work, fighting with a woman who has Down's syndrome. She wouldn't wash her dinner plate. WWIII practically broke out over that very plate. I wanted to murder her, kill her stone dead, wring her flamin' neck and then some.

I didn't tell her this. It's not proper to say such things.

I told her instead to wash her plate like a good lady.
She told me she wouldn't.
She told me to go to hell.
She told me to fuck off.
She told me she hated me.
Worst of all, she told me that she wouldn't get up for me the next morning.

I know her and her stubbornness. Nothing but the fire brigade would get her out of that bed if she took one of her notions to go to ground. I had a vision of bringing up the toaster and a basin of water to her room the following morning and prompting her dangling arm to fall into the water before I plugged in the toaster for an illuminating start to her day.

I love this place. This time away. The quiet earthedness, that rolling carpet of hill. The kissing of cottage garden flowers as they neck with each other near the elegant olde worlde stone wall.

I dig new potatoes in the garden. They tumble in euphoria on top of the humpty dumpty broken clay. Rubbery worms wriggle like short pink party streamers around and about them. The potatoes are delighted to be released from their Kingdom of Darkness. The worms, on the other hand, seem to know that underground is their friend and are writhing question marks of panic above ground. One beady-eyed robin flits onto the handle of the other spade. He'd like a takeaway. He knows he's in the right place for one.

The worms flee for their underground stations.

I am left here in my bent-backedness, thumbing the wet earth off the oriental-skinned potatoes before I hop them into the bucket. There will be steam and oh, courgettes!

Organic onions, carrots, garlic, celery, stock…There will be plummy voices on the radio, a composition by someone who's just played Carnegie Hall. There will be peace on earth, owls in trees, leaves frittering their last dance away on the sloping lawn. The sycamore weaving leaves and sky and branches against the window.

All this, there will be, soon and very soon, in my world.

In somebody else's world, there may be a spirited mutineer refusing point blank to wash her plate and some good person thinking of murdering her.

The Real Thing

*'Albert Mooney sez he loves her
All the boys are fightin' for her
Knock on the door, ring on the bell,
Oh my true love, are you well?'*

SHE DIDN'T KNOW where the words were coming from or whether she was even getting them half right, but it didn't matter one way or the other. Her name was Mary Cassidy, she was fourteen and in love.

The object of her affections was Padraig Devine. He was in fourth year. She was only in second. She couldn't remember how it had all started, when she had first began to see him as a god. It was probably on the school bus. A lot of things happened there; fights, friendships and lifelong feuds. The juddering vehicle saw a lot of action, there was no doubt about that. She sat on the left side of the bus, four seats down, nearly over the wheel. She usually stared mesmerised out the side window as the battered hedgerows blurred into green ribbons before her face, her forehead cool against the wet smeared coldness of the grimy glass.

Padraig Devine sat on the engine seat right next to the driver, his tanned skin almost luminous. His teeth were startlingly white when he smiled, which he did a lot. His black hair fell, shiny as a blackbird's wing, over the right side of his forehead. He absentmindedly ran his fingers through it from time to time to push it back, his stainless steel digital watch gleaming on his wrist as he did so. The gesture caught Mary's attention one day and from there she was hooked. No more watching hedgerows for her.

Although her glances at Padraig were covert, they took everything in. How straight he sat, the brown smoothness of his hand compared to the farmer-like pink ham of his companions. He never needed to hold on to the bar when he was getting off at the school. His balance was perfect. He was head and shoulders above the rest of them in appearance. Walking tall with an easy-going smile while the other lads walked with their heads low, hunched into their chests as if they were bottles with short stumpy stoppers. They 'shloothered'—as her mother would say—scraping their feet like shovels along the ground. They didn't walk properly. They hadn't a clue! And their trousers hung like deflated grey balloons from their backsides, usually embossed here and there with a darkened plastic patch of chewing gum. The official stamp of their hopelessness.

She didn't tell the girls at school. Not even Gemma and Alison. She couldn't bear the thought of them knowing that she fancied him. They'd scribble it in a busy body finger on the morning mist of a corridor window, that's what they do on her if she told them. And he'd see it with his mates and they'd all snigger.

Mary Cassidy loves Padraig Devine, it would say, inside a big loopy drawing of a heart.

She was going red just thinking about it. She could feel her stringy brown hair heating up against her cheek with the potential embarrassment. Her pale thin hands were getting anxiously moist at the very possibility. No, the thing about feelings was, you had to keep them to yourself. That's where everyone else went wrong, they told stuff out, trusted the wrong people. Not her. She told nobody anything and they'd stopped asking her anything. They took it for granted that because she was so quiet it left more room for her to listen to their love troubles. And that was fine. She listened with a day-dreaming ear to their latest 'I said to him and then he said to me...' topics as if they were the most fascinating subjects on earth. She clutched her commerce books to her scrawny body and imagined these situations were happening to her:

'And then I sez to Padraig,
And then Padraig sez to me...'

Oh, it was wonderful. She could see it happening. Really could. One day she would drop her homework journal 'accidentally on purpose' and he would 'happen' to be passing so he'd pick it up with a chivalrous smile and say 'It's Mary, isn't it? I've noticed you on the bus...'

And then he might look at the drawings she'd done on the cover of her journal – David Bowie and Queen and all them cool ones—and he'd say something like,

'wow! Did you do These?! These are great; you're really good at this art stuff...'

...And she'd reply with such brilliant witty wonderful answers that he'd barely be able to drag himself away from her riveting company...

...And she'd know that he was only dying to ask her out but couldn't find the words to...

...And she'd smile easily at him and say something cool like 'talk soon, ciao!' and swing her hair in a glossy curtain before turning and swishing gracefully down to the D area and the science labs...

...And it would all be so perfect!

She'd have no spots on her chin that day and her hair wouldn't look like shredded baler twine. His aquamarine eyes would stare into her brown gaze and they'd both know it was a special moment. The Real Thing. Of course he'd forget about all the other girls that were mad after him. Of course the hem wouldn't be coming down on her uniform skirt or the silly collar of her blouse buckling up at the edge like the corner of a battered copy book page. Her grey knee high socks wouldn't be at half mast and her legs wouldn't be blotchy red from the radiator. She wouldn't stutter once and she'd smell subtly of Nivea shampoo and Impulse body spray.

She practised her favourite words in her head:

Mrs Mary Devine, Mrs Mary Devine, Mrs Mary Devine... They sounded so right.

Alas, real life did not present her with the opportunities that her fantasies so kindly did. Whenever she met Padraig Devine in any corridor she walked deliberately faster, head down, pretending to study her name hard on the front of her top book or whatever else she had in her hands. Then she'd run into a girl's toilet as soon as she could and splash cold water on her face to get the horrid colour down. Sometimes Mary went so red she couldn't even see the freckles on her snub nose. And that was bad.

It was so unfair. The only boy in the whole school who ever spoke to her was smelly Timmy Brady. Everyone called him Goatspebbles, just for no reason. He had a rough reddened face like he was moulded out of damp pink chalk. There was always thread bits hanging out of his uniform jumper. And thin white maggoty lines of terrier hair all over him. His greasy hair had no shape nor make to it and the worst thing of all; he wiped his nose with the back of his hand. It made a big 'shloosh' noise when he did it. He smelt of sweat and staleness. He was horrible. For some hateful reason, he called her 'the Poisoned Dwarf' after that bitchy Lucy one on Dallas.

'Hi, Dwarf, how's life down there with you?' he'd ask her in his whiny bog accent whenever he'd meet her between classes.

She'd say something brilliant like 'shaddup' cos she could never think of anything else.

He sat behind her every day on the bus going home from school and she hated knowing that he was behind her, that his sick breath was blowing into her hair. Sometimes the thought alone made her wriggle uncomfortably and then she might feel him lean forward and say something like' 'hi, dwarf, the only part of you that's getting any bigger is your great fat head, move over, would ya, and let the rest of us see the daylight.'

And she'd say something brilliant like 'shaddup' all over again, go bright red and turn her face to the window, hoping to God that Padraig Devine couldn't see the horrible neon glow of her skin from his engine throne.

Something really awful happened. It was the day of the

Easter holidays. Because it was a Thursday she was running late after home economics. That old bat Mrs Carty always kept them late talking about carbohydrates and pure rubbish. By the time Mary got out of the cookery room in the B area, it meant she had to really leg it back up to the C area to put all her cookery books back in her locker, take out her homework stuff and run like blue blazes towards the assembly area to catch the bus. She seemed to be galloping against the crowd all the time and she could feel her eyes almost crazed with panic. She couldn't move fast enough. It would never do if she missed the bus! She had never missed it before. Her father wouldn't be able to pick her up. They had no phone at home, they wouldn't know what was keeping her late...it was such a long way, a long way; her feet would never make it, not with the weight of her bag...

Oh no. Oh no, oh no. No, no no.

She pushed and heaved against the crowd as if she were fighting her way through a blind herd of cattle. Finally slamming the door on her locker and now working her way vengefully towards the general assembly area, her arms full of loose books, her hair stringy, school bag swinging, anorak hanging askew... that's when she knew something was wrong. It took her a moment to cop it. A sense of something not quite right, a sliding sensation against her skin...

Oh Good God.

She knew now what it was.

The elastic had gone in her knickers.

No, no, no, not today, Lord! Not to me!

But yes, it had happened today and to her.

Mary slowed down her pace, her eyes almost filling with tears at her helplessness; she walked wide-legged like a cowboy, holding disaster at bay.

And on and on and on.

Each step a long wide one, a walk of a girl going to her own public execution.

She could see from the front car park that the bus was just

starting to pull off, that dense blue smoke panting from its exhaust. She shuffled towards it, bubbles of frustration on her desperate lips as she formed an internal scream.

Wait! Wait! Wait! her mind shouted, but all the time her mouth felt as dry as Gandhi's flip-flop and she couldn't utter a syllable aloud.

It was as if somebody heard her.

The bus stopped its lumbering motion and remained shuddering like a big clumsy yellow animal on the tarmac.

She continued her slow advance, her hips swinging in wide arcs to keep the treacherous hula hoop nature of her knickers in place. She mounted the bus with beads of sweat on her upper lip.

'Thanks,' she muttered in a husky croak to the bus driver, and then succeeded in reaching her seat without the worst happening.

She couldn't bear to look up towards Padraig Devine, see whether he was laughing at her and if he was, how loudly. Such an embarrassment – her nearly getting left behind.

And what was she going to do about the other Thing?

'You think you're a right cool bitch, keeping us all waitin'. Well, you're a stuck-up wee runt, so y'are,' said a horrible tin voice in her right ear. Timmy Brady.

'Ah shaddup,' she said brilliantly, turning her face to the window and trying as best she could to cool her blazing cheek against the cold condensation on the glass.

It was the most terrifying journey of her life.

How would she leave the bus? She would need to hold on to the bar near the door with one hand, she surely couldn't be clutching her skirt with the other; she had her folders to carry? Oh God, she didn't feel at all well.

She panicked furiously to herself, debated and prayed for the entire twelve mile trip.

It seemed that in no time it was upon her – the final bend for home. The crooked whitethorn at Jamesie Farrelly's lane, her cue to stand up and move forward.

Except she couldn't. Why couldn't she?

She was jerking her head forward with all her might but she couldn't free herself from the seat behind.

She could hear Timmy Brady's raspy old laugh, *ha ha ha.*

'That'll keep you down to size, dwarf,' he said.

Ha, ha, ha.

She jerked and jerked then somehow she figured it out. He had knotted the cords of her anorak hood to the bar running right behind her seat. He had trapped her.

The bus had stopped now. They were all waiting. All looking.

'You get that off me right now, you dirty fecker,' she hissed furiously back at him, overcome with anger and humiliation. So hurt that there were no tears in her eyes and she was trembling with white hot rage. She unzipped her anorak and wriggled out of it, turning with whiplash speed to sort out the catastrophe herself.

'Hi! Let that lassie go, would ya!' shouted the bus driver from the rear view mirror.

Timmy Brady's big red hands were fumbling uselessly at the knot now and he was the one looking embarrassed. Mary yanked the anorak as hard as she could, tearing it completely free of the bar snapping the cord with a furious nylon 'zing' sound.

She stood up to her full height and with a fury born of years of three years loathing and this one unforgivable incident of pure humiliation, she shaped her right hand into a tight snarl of a fist, drew out with all the passion in her small quivering frame and punched Timmy Brady straight in the mouth. She could feel the wet jellied impact of her flesh against his lip, her knuckle grazing the resistance of his teeth, the sheer slam of her blow pushing his horrible face out of shape, his bulging eyes surprised.

'How's that for size?' she snarled at him, her voice not afraid to carry its anger to all present. A loud cheer went up for her as she turned and walked up the narrow aisle. Slowly, deliberately, using her John Wayne walk, one hand coolly on her hip as she kept potential disaster at bay, her other clasping her hand-

drawn Bon Jovi folders nobly to her breast. She was so stunned
with herself as she moved forward that she looked dead ahead
at Padraig Devine. Dead ahead. His face loomed like the Sacred
Heart in front of her.

Smiling.

At her.

It was all she could focus on, those stunning blue eyes. His
huge smile with those even white bread teeth. Oh God, was all
truly lost now?

Padraig Devine winked at her.

Padraig Devine said, 'atta girl, that fella had it comin' to him.'

Padraig Devine looked at her the way a man looks at a woman
on those soppy TV dramas.

Then Padraig Devine said 'Bye, Mary...'

She got off the bus dazedly but still having enough of her wits
to step it out like Mae West until she heard the heavy engine
lumbering finally over the hill. Only the belching exhaust fumes
remaining, incensing this sacred moment. Then she broke out
into a fit of elated laughter.

Padraig Devine knew her name!

Padraig Devine looked at her in That kind of way!

Padraig Devine didn't like Timmy Brady either!

Padraig Devine loved her! She loved Padraig Devine!

No doubt about it, this was the Real Thing alright. She had
never felt so good in all her life.

Mary put her hand on her hip again and swayed her way
blissfully home.

'Oh my true love, are you well,
Oh my true love, are you well?!'

MY ANCESTORS

ONE MONASTERY MORNING, my earring falls down behind my desk. Damned if I'm losing another one. I yank and pull and pull and yank the desk out from the wall and discover a small plastic American flag, a lip gloss and a folded up sheet of paper.

I line them up on my desk and wonder about them. When I unfold the paper, it has an entire side of itself covered in handwritten notes for a possible talk or essay. For some reason I judge the writing to be feminine. The content is rather pedestrian. Yet I sense that the writer knows more than he/she is putting on the paper or distilling from other sources. There is a lot of heavy scribbling out, as if fishing for simpler ways to state the message. Here, I feel, is a mind that is shaving part of itself off to give to others. There is deliberate simplification. I wonder what age group this writer is appealing to. Adult but dim is what I'm conjecturing. Possibly people like me. People who don't often look towards the metaphorical stars. Folks who need to be reminded slowly and in deliberate ways, look up, look outwards, no matter how tall your grandfather was you still have your own growing to do.

God is mentioned in her notes. But I forget now quite how he came into the whole equation. God's a bit like that. You know, like you're looking back at photos from a great party about which you really remember very little and there, in the background of quite a few is God. And you're saying to yourself:

'There's that God fellow again. How come He gets himself into all the pictures?'

Or maybe you're saying to yourself:

'There's that God fellow again. Who the hell invited Him?' On top of that, I wonder about the paper being folded. What kind of writing mind folds their paper? I sense that the writer had perhaps a little bit of loosening up to do themselves. I picture her pacing the hermitage. She is bandbox smart, a life that presents as apple-pie order, long ash grey hair tied back in some kind of loose knot while she unravels her thoughts in front of the long window. She smokes a pen because she's given up real cigarettes over ten years ago and remains superbly in control of everything to do with nicotine. She tries to focus on the academic side of her being here and what all she must achieve before she catches the 10.20 flight from Denver to New York next Thursday but every now and then the emptiness encroaches and as has been her habit for so many years she firmly folds away those thoughts into sharp creases and slides them back into unseen places.

But did she wear the lipstick?

No. That was someone else. A different woman altogether. My first woman came from the north, maybe somewhere easterly like Maine or New York, My lipstick lady comes from a more sunshine state. I can hear her talking with a drawl, her hair is lacquered into perfection to just under her earlobes. Even in the hermitage she wears her jewellery, applies foundation, mascara, takes an hour to apply coral pink varnish to both finger and toe nails. The only time in her life where she finds stillness is when she waits for the polish to set. She flaps her fingers and wiggles her toes from the tilted viewpoint of the Lay-z-boy, continuing to shake long after the varnish is actually dry. She finds it hard to be away from her groups. She misses her props. The phone, the mall, *Oprah*, the girls in the spinning class, her programmes, her catalogs, her mail. Even the sound of her shoes. Here, the sand swallows all footsteps. There is no place for click clacking. She has had to ditch her beloved Manolos and come down in the world with some sad flip flop efforts she bought at the last minute in Denver. But at least they're pink and match her polish. She's seven months into her legal separation and going strong. She owns half a house and half a condo in Boca Raton and whole of nothing anywhere. But she's got good credit and a better lawyer. She's going to bleed the bastard dry. Here in the hermitage she spends her 'filling-in time' calculating the prospective financial settlement less tax and expenses on the monastery stationary. She's not really into God but that doesn't bother her. It was her friend Sylvia, a Buddhist, who recommended this place in Colorado. My Lipstick lady is not really into finding herself because she doesn't happen to think she's particularly lost but she just wanted to be away from any place she'd ever been with him.

The flag then?

It belonged to a man, that much I know. He is middle-aged, fair haired but balding. He seems to be the worrying kind. Possibly he worries professionally, I'm not sure. Maybe he's an acountant, a religion teacher or a counsellor. He carries anxiety like tight little sandbags all over his personality and he will not be lifted into anything that is not perfectly serious and matter of fact. I get the impression that he's strongly involved in his church back home and that it was his parish priest who recommended this place to him. The flag was packed into his bag by his youngest son - let's call him Cody - just minutes before he left for the airport. Cody had a missionary zeal when it came to passing around flags these days. Ever since 9 11 he sees it as his personal duty that the Stars and Stripes flutters from every house in their suburb. So here is this man, waving its sorry flimsy plastic while he sits at the hermitage desk and tries not to be so aware of its hysterical profusion all over his country. Even here, thanks to his son, no getting away from the silent terror.

Is it months later that I find these people's relics? Or years? Where are the retreatants who needed these props? Blown like dandelion clocks back towards their own worlds, their old mindsets, or new jobs and lives, new husbands and wives?

On the fourth of July I bring the small plastic American flag to the parade in downtown Crestone. As an Irish woman I am very supportive of waving anything in the name of Independence. Yet as an adult, it feels strange having a flag, waving it. Especially a cheap replica of the flag representing the most powerful country in the world. A country that can evoke so much anger, gratitude, ridicule, disbelief. But it is the country that gave my father the price of his farm. That continues to support many unknown branches of my family who would otherwise have struggled through existences back in Ireland. A country that has provided me with some of the happiest memories in my life. I wave it for my father, for the love he had for this country and for my American friends whom I love. Somewhere on the crowded sun-pecked Crestone streets, I lose that flag. I only hope it was a child who picked it up.

They know better than we what to do with it.

DEATH AND HOW TO SURVIVE IT

DEATH is a theme that has revisited my life with monotonous regularity over the past number of years. My immediate family - by which I mean my mother, father, my only brother and his wife have all been disposed of by one common denominator—death.

My mother, prematurely to cancer aged sixty.

My father, age-related complications, aged eighty.

My brother, tragically, aged thirty six and his wife, prematurely to cancer one year before him, aged thirty five.

I write that much down to honour them.

Looking at the print is hard. Looking at it and knowing that this has all happened, that the stories around each of these lives and deaths are welded like the spectacles of holocaust victims in my psyche, that is very hard.

I don't want to look back. I want to move on. Maybe that's why graves are so hard to visit. The cold names in print bring us back to the bare bones of our stories, the memories gear up into internal home movies.

My father, if you ask me, was the only one of them to die 'properly' and at the right time. For years and years he had been looking forward to death with ghoulish appetite.

He pictured the headstone. Marble. He pictured the cause. The Heart.

He always wanted a Sunday funeral. Good attendance guaranteed.

Towards the end of October 1996, I got the phone call saying that he had 'taken bad' quite suddenly and was rambling and raving and barely conscious. He had been brought down to Cavan hospital in an ambulance. I knew when I heard that much that this was it. It was confirmed when my sister-in-law told me that he had been seeing a woman in the room for the past few days beckoning him towards the window. Apparently he'd also been visited by a little girl called Mary.

Mary was his baby sister who died when only a few years old.

When I heard this, it told me beyond all doubt that it was his time to go. What's more, I knew he would die on the 31st October, which would be five years to the very day of my mother's death. My father was a great one for performance and I figured that even his death would be timed right for maximum effect. I was glad for him, If he got his timing right, this would also give him a Sunday funeral.

By the time I reached the hospital he was unconscious in the cardiac ward, breathing through an oxygen mask that bit a red irregular oval mark into his swollen face. Monitors beeped, sank and expanded all round him in their macabre version of life. A drip fed his arm and he seemed to have tubes coming from all angles. It was horrific to see a big man so utterly helpless, everything being done for him by machinery. The nurse said he had come to at one point and seemed 'very afraid.' I held his hand now - hot, damp, white, so unlike his real working hand—unable to touch his fear but wishing him free of it.

It was not his place to be afraid. He was always the tower of strength, the one who knew what to do, what to confront; never, ever afraid, not him.

They moved him into a private room after they told us there was nothing they could do. I sat up with him the first night alone. He had not regained consciousness since I had come. I was sorry I would never say goodbye or have the chance to thank him properly. It is so Irish of me, but I had never told him that I loved him. I told him now, whispered it into his ear. It was fractionally better than I had managed with my mother. I hadn't got telling her until she was dead. In both cases, it felt way too late to let these wonderful people know how much they meant to me and that the many sacrifices that they had made for me all through my life were appreciated.

The second night, the doctors thought his vitals were deteriorating rapidly. He might just make it through another twenty four hours, they thought. Prepare yourselves, they said.

A gang of old men—friends and relations—gathered round the end of my fathers' bed and started racing through a fleet of rosaries. It was like the Grand National of prayer events. As someone commented once, it's amazing how Irish people can say the first half of a Hail Mary on an out breath and then with a sucked in re-grouping, get the second half said on a hissing in breath. It saves time. And souls.

The old men said they'd seen other men like my father last for weeks.

He didn't have the death rattle, they said. A good sign.

He could make it till the weekend, maybe even, if God was good, till the middle of next week. He had a strong heart, for all the angina and cholesterol.

He could pull through yet, they said, *you never knew.*

They got up, almost looking somewhat disappointed and said their goodbyes in shuffling droves at ten pm. Each one in turn lifting his huge hand in floppy inert handshakes and making the sign of the cross at him. When they left, I rubbed my father's hand again and said to him,

'Do you really want to be here till next week with them fellows talkin' about you? Let go, daddy, go to Josie. She's waiting for you. Just forgive him before you go. Just forgive him.'

I knew there was just one person on my father's mind whom he had not made his peace with. On his mind for years. Snaring his heart like ivy. I felt this was at the root of his fear.

'Forgive him,' I said again—but deeply mortified at being the one telling my father what to do. I felt really stupid saying it. No one in this world ever told him what to do - 'And let yourself go with Josie, be at peace. You know you're ready to leave me. I love you, daddy. Thank you for every single thing. Please let me know you've forgiven him. Please.'

It was barely a couple of moments later when I felt the grip of his fingers strengthen between mine. I looked in surprise at my father's face, struggling as if with huge effort, the eyes opened for a flicker, but straight at me. I felt terrified. It was like he was about to say something. I saw that fear through his eyes. But then it was gone again, eyes closed. His hand slackened in mine. He had one massive convulsion lasting a few seconds and then he was gone, really really gone. The colour that had suffused his face left it. Pale and, I hoped, finally at peace.He was cued up for a Sunday funeral and the old boy network would be quite surprised to hear that he had died less than ten minutes after they'd left the room. They had been cheated out of that eerie moment of watching a life depart. I felt honoured to be alone with him. His timing was perfect.

It was a year later.

Hallow E'en evening and I was at my home in Sligo town. I went out of the back yard, shutting Riley the dog into the kitchen and then slamming the yard door behind me as I popped into my neighbours back kitchen to hear her litany of giving out about *them feckin' trick or treaters and all the bangers and stuff going off and what the hell kind of buck eegits did they have for parents anyway.*

I visited with her for about half an hour then came back to my own back yard gate against which—inexplicably—a stick was propped up.

I lifted it absently, thinking that Riley must have fetched it from some strange place and left it there to remind us how great he was. Then my brain clicked into gear as I realised that I'd left the dog inside.

So it wasn't him.

The main gate to the roadway was locked, no one else could

get into the back common yard and it was such a mild evening, no wind blowing, no sizeable sticks hurling themselves though the air. It didn't make sense until I had opened my back door and patted Riley on the head. It was when I told him I'd only been out visiting Betty that my heart gave a lurch and I felt my whole body shudder with the memory.

Every time my father made a visit in his lifetime, if the person he was going to visit wasn't home, he left what he called 'his calling card'.

A stick propped up at their door.

This was my father's first anniversary.

I knew he was safe, home and at peace. I felt that he had forgiven and been forgiven back. And to prove it, he was still doing what he loved best, getting out and about on those social visits. It would take a man as strong-willed as he to prove that there is indeed some class of social life after death.

Handwritten Lives

THE LETTER RACK in the middle window was a clock for the seasons.

It held test cards, imminent cattle sales, welcome letters from far-off friends, over-sized Christmas cards from the U.S.A., tissue-thin blue and red airmail letters and weighty relic and prayer-card filled envelopes from the nun in Drogheda.

Little pieces of other lives crept into the window in words to my mother. She was a great correspondent herself.

She sometimes let me read the letters she received.

I loved the lives that came across to me in writing. A lot of these hand-writers had worked with her when she was nursing in the life she lived before she got married. These correspondents referred to old co-workers with great enthusiasm and involvement but their references to my father, brother and I were strained and removed. *Clare must be getting big now. Does she like school all that much? Who does she take after, your side or Phil's? Does your Eddie show an interest in the farm?*

The reason for these stiff comments was easy enough to understand. They had only encountered me in photographs. I may have never met them in person, but I judged them now by their way with words, or even the style of their script.

The woman down in Kilkenny was loop the loop, all over

the place. Her thoughts were scattered, even on paper. What kind of a nurse must she have been? I pictured her as having big fluffy blonde hair and a blouse missing a button somewhere, tight nylon trousers, bright coloured with a cheap sheen, that kind of thing.

The woman in Australia was very together, extremely neat, very family-oriented, but a bit too holy for my liking. She probably had tight hair and wore twin sets and an eighteen hour girdle, or else was as thin as a twig and very conscious of the importance of fibre and regular bowel motions. I just knew her house would be full of knitting patterns and stomach powders.

I enjoyed the letters from Middlesex, England. They were the ones that saw the humour in life. I had actually met this woman and could hear her fast-paced English accent telling us through the written words about her son going for his driving test in central London and −oh my Lord − crashing into the back of a BMW.

'Naturally, he didn't pass,' she wrote, *'and I can't say we were at all surprised.'*

Her family moved around the world with rucksacks and saw everything, worked with everyone, camped everywhere, took diseases, got better, went back to University, met new girl-friends, broke up, met other ones, settled down, got great jobs and had blonde English children.

I loved the whole glorious unfolding of these handwritten lives.

They were as real as my own.

I have taken that love of handwriting with me into adult life. Even now, when I get a letter, a real letter, I make a huge ceremony out of studying the postage stamp, the slant of the writing, the whole ambiance before I carefully pull it open. Depending on the thickness of the envelope, I may deem it imperative to have a mug of coffee beside me on the table by the time I unfold the notepaper, preparatory to inhaling the first word, the mood.

Through several house moves in my life, the one thing I have refused to shed is my stash of personal letters. To me, they are more valuable than photographs.

Even in my mind's eye I can still clearly see my mother's script when she used to write to me in college. Her writing was tall and elegant. She went to town on her capital 'C' in particular and her ability to take up an entire envelope with my name and address was akin to seeing my name up in lights in London's West End. There was a period in my second year that she wouldn't write to me because she refused to believe that my new address of 'The Housewife's Choice, Wine St, Sligo' could be a real one. She wouldn't swallow the truth that *The Housewife's Choice* was a grocery shop of great Sligonian importance or that an Irish street could be named after alcohol. The onus was on me to convince her as soon as possible with an official domestic bill. This was a matter of great urgency to me because if I hadn't done so, no homely news embellished with twenty pound notes would've come my way at times of near student insolvency.

I scrutinised her letters at this time with the dedication of a graphologist. She had a forgetful habit of resting her pen nib on the paper after each word, leaving a tiny circle of ink. To me, it was emotional Morse code. I wondered more about what was not being said in the words. The pause between them that caused her to rest her pen for whatever length of time spoke more than she could ever put in writing. It was literally a case of reading between the words because my college years were the ones during which she underwent two major operations and the chemo and radiation that followed them. Her letters from home were my only clues as to what might be going on for her. She never expressed unwellness in her correspondence and I could only guess what the true story was. I pictured her writing a word, stopping, writing a word, stopping.

There must have been a thousand unspoken thoughts between every word she wrote.

It's not that long since I was clearing myself out of another house, packing up all my earthly goods and chattels. Putting my jigsaw life into box after box, I was surprised out of my maudlin reveries somewhat by a single sheet of blue Basildon Bond note-paper floating through the air from its nesting place in some unread book or other.

I picked it up. It was the second page from one of my mother's letters to me way back at least fifteen years ago. Orphaned from the leading page, it contained only a couple of closing lines:

'*We are all well here. Hope you are happy there. Let us know if you need anything,*

Love, Mother.'

ALSO BY CLARE LYNCH:

SHORT STEPS IN LONG GRASS
BLACK BATTLER PRESS 2002

www.clarelynch.com

About the Author

Clare Lynch was born in Co. Cavan but has lived in Sligo for many years. Author of *Short Steps in Long Grass* (Black Battler press 2002), her work is also featured in anthologies by the Knocknarea Women Writers (*badel 2003*) and Writers Ink group (*Dolly Mixtures 2004*).

Clare has had work featured on *Sunday Miscellany*, RTE Radio 1, *The Quiet Quarter*, RTE Lyric Fm and *Arthouse, Ocean Fm*. She has also had her pieces recorded by The National Council for the Blind. Her writing has been published in *Force 10*, *Desert Call* and *Sacred Journey*. Runner-up in *The Ireland's Own* International Short Story competition in 2002, she was overall winner in 2005. She owns a cat and ties her own shoelaces.